D0320865

SCHOOLS COUNCIL
MODULAR COURSES IN TECHNOLOGY
MECHANISMS

Omry Bailey

Roy Pickup

Ray Lewis

Peter Patient

Oliver & Boyd

in association with the National Centre for School Technology

PROJECT TEAM

Director
Dr Ray Page

Co-ordinators
Roy Pickup
John Poole

Jeffrey Hall
Dr Duncan Harris
John Hucker
Michael Ive
Peter Patient

St. Mary's College
Trench House
Belfast BT11 9GA

Oliver & Boyd
Robert Stevenson House
1–3 Baxter's Place
Leith Walk
Edinburgh EH1 3BB

A Division of Longman Group UK Ltd

ISBN 0 05 003386 7

First published 1981
Eighth impression 1987

© SCDC Publications 1981
All rights reserved.
No part of this publication may be reproduced,
stored in a retrieval system, or transmitted
in any form or by any means, electronic,
mechanical, photocopying, recording or
otherwise, without prior written
permission of the Publishers.

Produced by Longman Group (FE) Ltd
Printed in Hong Kong

Contents

Note   The sign ■ has been used in the text to signify material suitable for both O-level and CSE candidates. The sign □ indicates material required only for the O-level examination.

Introduction

ST. MARY'S COLLEGE
TRENCH HOUSE
BELFAST BT11 9GA

■ Man the Toolmaker

One of the factors which distinguishes human beings from other animals is their ability to make and use tools. Stone tools were used by early man for defence, hunting and preparing meat for food. The tools extended his bodily powers and enabled him to achieve things not possible with his bare hands. From these early and seemingly crude beginnings we have achieved a degree of control over many things on Earth. We now bear a huge responsibility not to misuse this control, and to protect our future and that of every living thing on Earth.

■ The First Machines

Thousands of years ago machines of one kind or another were used to help build temples and monuments and to irrigate the fields. Early attempts to move heavy stones could well have resulted in the discovery that a branch of a tree can be used as a lever.   Some ancient civilizations were renowned as engineers and builders. For example, the Egyptians of around 2500 BC had metal tools and wheeled carriages. We know from the impressive pyramids of the Nile Valley that their engineering techniques were well developed. Enormous stones were hewn from the ground and moved great distances to build the pyramids. Similarly, the early Britons moved gigantic stones to erect great structures such as Stonehenge.

Fig. 1   'In the beginning . . .'

Fig. 2   The pyramids – an improbable
solution to a big problem

Fig. 3   Stonehenge – how were the stones
lifted?

Huge stones were probably moved on tree trunks laid as rollers. Rollers under heavy stones enable the load to be moved with less effort. Roller tracks are still widely used today.

Fig. 4   The use of rollers to move heavy stone blocks – a smaller force is needed as the friction is reduced.

Early civilizations developed the **wheel** from rollers. The wheels on ancient carts were probably sections of tree trunk attached to an axle (Fig. 5).

Fig. 5   The development of the wheel

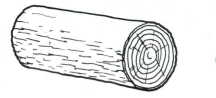

Wheeled chariots were certainly being used in the Middle East about 2500 BC, The use of animals to provide the energy to pull heavy loads on wheeled carts became common in the Middle Ages (Fig. 6). In the nineteenth century, animal power began to be superseded by machines such as the steam engine.

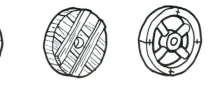

Fig. 6   An ancient type of wheeled cart

The **pulley** may have developed from the idea of throwing a rope over a tree branch and attaching it to a load. When a pull force is applied to the load, the load is raised. The pulley shown in Fig. 7 changes the direction of the action of the applied force. The force in the rope is a **tension force**.

Fig. 7   A method of lifting water from a well

Fig. 8   The windlass

One development of the pulley is the **windlass** (Fig. 8). This might be used to raise water from wells. A rope attached to the load is wound round a wooden cylinder. The cylinder is rotated by a cranked handle.

Another type of pulley is the **wheel and axle** (Fig. 9) where a long rope passes over a large diameter wheel. Another rope is attached to the smaller diameter axle. The leverage provided by the large wheel fixed to the smaller axle enables heavy loads to be raised with a small effort.

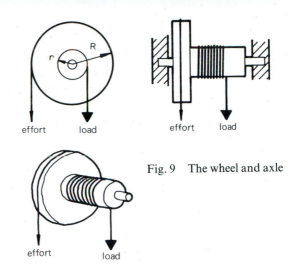

Fig. 9   The wheel and axle

The raising of heavy loads, such as blocks of stone, to great heights was achieved in ancient times by the use of a slope called an **inclined plane**. Early builders constructed the slope and then, using rollers, they gradually moved the stones into position (Fig. 10).

Fig. 10   The use of an inclined plane

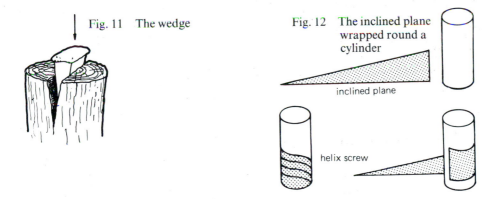

A development of the inclined plane is the **wedge**. This has many uses, for example to split logs (Fig. 11).

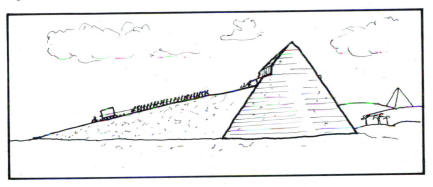

Fig. 11   The wedge

Fig. 12   The inclined plane wrapped round a cylinder

inclined plane

helix screw

When an inclined plane is wrapped round a cylinder, its edge produces a helix shape (Fig. 12). A **screw** is an example of the use of this type of inclined

7

plane. An Ancient Greek called Archimedes is believed to have invented a water-raising device using the principle of the screw (Fig. 13). Archimedes' screw is still used today to raise water to irrigate land, and as a feed mechanism in mincers, injection moulders and solid fuel stoking systems.

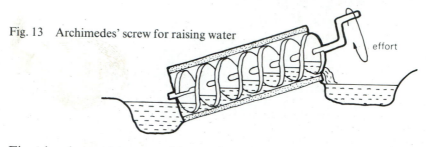

Fig. 13   Archimedes' screw for raising water

Five simple machines used by ancient civilizations have been described. They are the lever, windlass, pulley, wedge and screw.

■ Motion

Machines and mechanisms can be described in terms of the kind of motion they produce. **Linear motion** is motion in a straight line. An arrow is used to indicate linear motion. Steady linear motion is known as velocity, i.e. uniform motion in a straight line.

1 What units are used to measure velocity?

If the linear motion is backwards and forwards, it is called **reciprocating motion**. It is indicated by a line with an arrowhead on each end.

Motion in a circle is called **rotary motion**. It can be indicated by a curved line with an arrowhead on each end. The number of complete revolutions made in a known time, usually revolutions per minute (**revs/min**), is called the rotary velocity.

Motion backwards and forwards in a circular arc is called **oscillating motion**. It can be indicated by a double-headed curved arrow.

These four types of motion are illustrated in Fig. 14.

Fig. 14   Types of motion

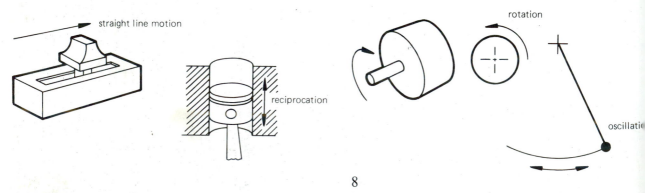

2   *What kind of motion occurs in the following situations or devices?*
    a) Hand drill or wheel brace.
    b) Child on a garden swing or a rocking horse.
    c) Pencil drawn along a ruler.
    d) Needle on a sewing machine.

■ Machines and Mechanisms

Five ancient machines were mentioned earlier. Their purpose was to move loads. To do this, they required an input of energy.

3   *What were the five ancient machines?*

A **machine** is a device which does work by converting or transmitting energy. A bicycle, a lawn mower, a brace and bit, a hand drill, an egg whisk and a lathe are examples of machines. All machines are made up of mechanisms. Even very large and complex machines consist of a number of basically simple mechanisms or working parts. The lever, pulley, gear, cam, screw and ratchet are all basic mechanisms. A **mechanism** transforms an input motion and force into a desired output motion and force. Sometimes an output force is not required, e.g. in a pressure gauge or aneroid barometer. Only output motion is required. The input force overcomes friction and moves and supports only the components of the device.

■ Engines

Engines are types of machines. An **engine** is a machine that converts a naturally occurring form of energy, e.g. a fuel, into useful work. Such engines are called **prime movers**. For example, a water wheel converts the energy of moving water into rotational movement so that the water wheel turns stones to grind grain. A steam engine turns the chemical energy of coal into the heat energy which is stored in steam. The steam drives the piston of the engine. The reciprocating motion of the piston is transformed into the rotary motion of the wheels. Figure 15 shows a complex machine consisting of an engine and many simple mechanisms.

Fig. 15   A model steam
            traction engine

Answers to Questions
1   Metres per second (m/s).
2   *a)* Rotary motion.
    b) Oscillating motion.
    c) Linear motion.
    d) Reciprocating motion.
3   Lever, windlass, pulley, wedge and screw.

9

1 Levers and Linkages

■ The Lever

A **lever** is a rigid rod pivoted about a fixed axis called a **fulcrum** (Fig. 1.1).

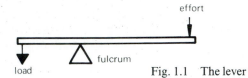

Fig. 1.1   The lever

A lever can produce a small output motion from a large input motion. For example, on the handbrake of a soap-box cart (Fig. 1.2a), a large hand movement is required to move the brake block a small distance on to the tyre of the wheel. Likewise, the handbrake lever on a car requires a large movement in order to move the brake cable a small amount (Fig. 1.2b).

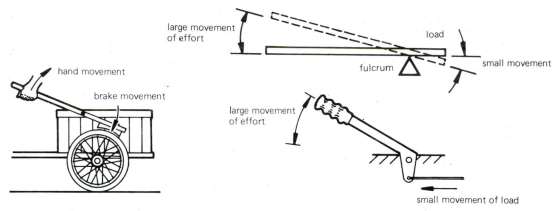

Fig. 1.2   a) A handbrake lever on a soap-box cart   b) A car handbrake lever

A lever can be used the other way round. A small input movement can be increased by a lever and result in a large output movement. For example, an aneroid barometer uses a lever to amplify the small movements of a partially evacuated metal capsule caused by changes in atmospheric pressure (Fig. 1.3). This results in large movements of the pointer on the scale.

Fig. 1.3   a) An aneroid barometer   b) The lever as an amplifier

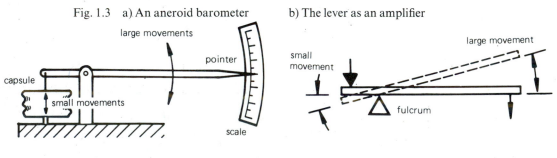

The ratio of the amount of movement made by the effort to the amount of movement made by the load is called the **velocity ratio**.

$$\text{Velocity ratio} = \frac{\text{distance moved by the effort}}{\text{distance moved by the load}}.$$

A lever is acted upon by two forces – the **load** and the **effort**. By suitably positioning the fulcrum, a small effort can move a large load (Fig. 1.4). This arrangement provides what is called a mechanical advantage. The ratio of the two forces, load and effort, is called the **mechanical advantage** of the lever.

Fig. 1.4   a) The lever   b) Diagram of a lever

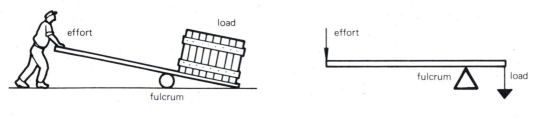

$$\text{Mechanical advantage} = \frac{\text{load}}{\text{effort}}.$$

Example
A packing case weighing 600 newtons is lifted by a man using a crowbar (Fig. 1.4a). The man pushes down with an effort of 200 newtons. The mechanical advantage of the crowbar is

$$\frac{600 \text{ newtons}}{200 \text{ newtons}} = 3.$$

There is a price to pay for gaining mechanical advantage when a small effort moves a large load. The distance moved by the smaller effort is greater than the distance moved by the larger load.

■ **Types of Lever**

There are **three classes of lever**. Each class has the fulcrum, effort and load arranged in a different way. The three classes are shown in Fig. 1.5.

Fig. 1.5   The three classes of lever

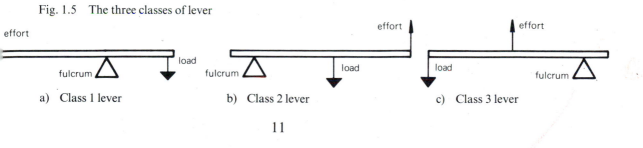

a)   Class 1 lever   b)   Class 2 lever   c)   Class 3 lever

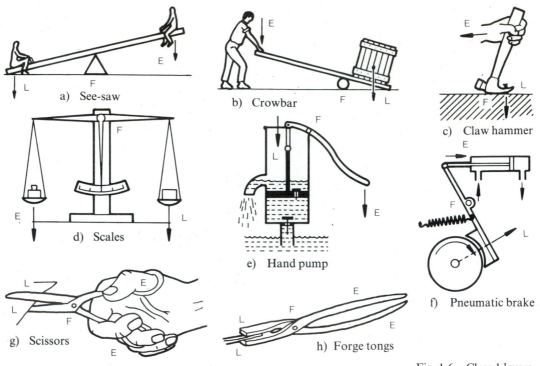

Fig. 1.6   Class 1 levers

Practical examples of the three classes of lever are shown in Fig. 1.6 (Class 1 levers), Fig. 1.7 (Class 2 levers), and Fig. 1.8 (Class 3 levers).

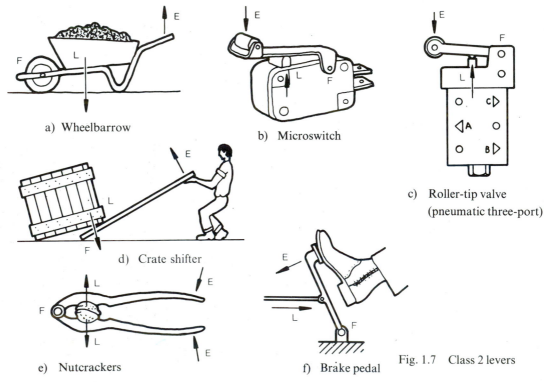

Fig. 1.7   Class 2 levers

12

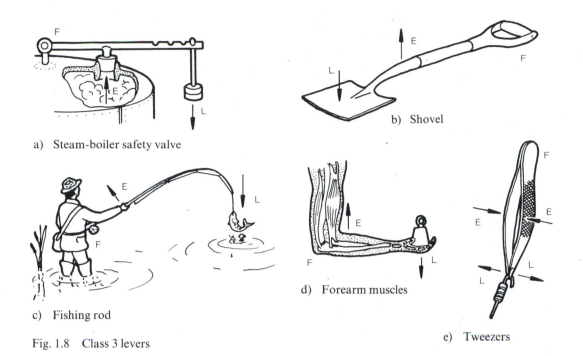

a) Steam-boiler safety valve

b) Shovel

c) Fishing rod

d) Forearm muscles

e) Tweezers

Fig. 1.8   Class 3 levers

Notice that some of the illustrations show double levers such as scissors, tongs, nut crackers and tweezers.

Figs. 1.9 and 1.10 show levers in use in a machine. What classes of lever are being used?

Fig. 1.9   A small hydraulic pump

Fig. 1.10   A pneumatic injection
moulding machine

13

■ The Bell Crank Lever

The **bell crank lever** is a right-angled Class 1 lever. The name 'bell crank' comes from the time when the bell crank lever was used as part of a system to call servants. The input motion is transmitted through a right angle to give an output motion (Fig. 1.11).

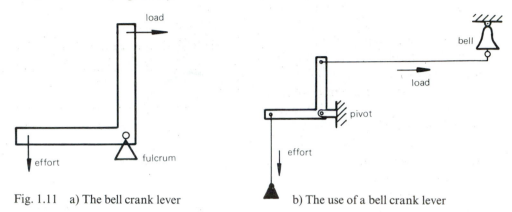

Fig. 1.11   a) The bell crank lever   b) The use of a bell crank lever

A double version of the bell crank lever is shown in Fig. 1.12a. A bell crank lever is used in altimeters which measure the height of an aircraft. The altimeter works on a principle similar to an aneroid barometer. A capsule expands with a decrease in atmospheric pressure and contracts with an increase in atmospheric pressure (Fig. 1.12b).

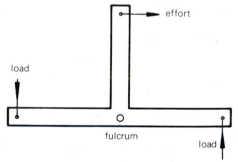

Another use of a bell crank lever is in older railway signalling systems. A wire or rod connects the lever and the railway signal or points. Operation of the lever moves the points or alters the signal (Fig. 1.13).

Fig. 1.12   a) The double bell crank lever
b) The altimeter

Fig. 1.13   A railway signal lever

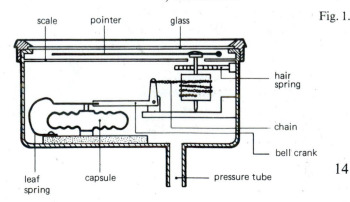

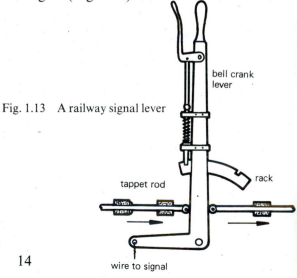

14

Moments and Levers

When a body is at rest under the action of forces, it is in **equilibrium** (Fig. 1.14). Consider a lever in equilibrium with an effort on one side of the fulcrum and a load on the other side. The load force in Fig. 1.15 tends to turn the lever in a clockwise direction. The effort tends to turn it in an anticlockwise direction. The turning effects balance one another and the equilibrium is not disturbed. The product of force and distance from the pivot point, or fulcrum, is called the **moment** of the force. For a lever to be in equilibrium the clockwise moments about the fulcrum must equal the anticlockwise moments.

Fig. 1.14   Equilibrium

Fig. 1.15   Moments acting on a lever

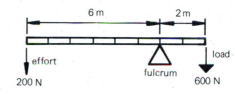

Example

Figure 1.15 shows a lever where an effort of 200 N balances a load of 600 N. The effort force is 6 metres from the fulcrum. The load force is 2 metres from the fulcrum.

Clockwise moment about the fulcrum = 600×2 N m.
Anticlockwise moment about the fulcrum = 200×6 N m.
In a state of equilibrium,
clockwise moments = anticlockwise moments
$$600 \times 2 \text{ N m} = 200 \times 6 \text{ N m}$$
$$1200 = 1200.$$

The principle of moments can help in design problems.

Example
The maximum mass to be hung on the load side of a steelyard is 10 kg (a weight of $10 \times g$ newtons where g is the acceleration due to gravity). The balancing mass is 1 kg (a weight of $1 \times g$ newtons). The load is hung 100 mm (0.1 m) from the pivot. How long does the steelyard need to be?

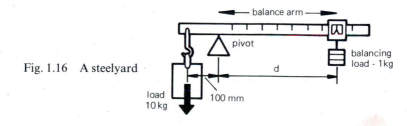

Fig. 1.16   A steelyard

Let the balance arm be d metres long, then
clockwise moments about the pivot $= 1 \text{ kg} \times 9.81 \times d \, (\text{N m})$,
anticlockwise moments about the pivot $= 10 \text{ kg} \times 9.81 \times 0.1 \text{ m} \, (\text{N m})$.
In equilibrium, clockwise moments = anticlockwise moments,
$$9.81 \times d = 10 \times 9.81 \times 0.1,$$
$$d = 10 \times 0.1 = 1.$$
Therefore, $d = 1$ metre.
The steelyard needs to be at least $1 + 0.1$ metres long.

Example
A crowbar lever is used to move a
400 N load (Fig. 1.17). The crowbar is
2.1 m long and the fulcrum is 0.6 m
from one end. What effort is required
to move the load? What is the
mechanical advantage of the crowbar?

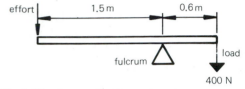

Fig. 1.17   A crow-bar lever

Taking moments about the fulcrum,
clockwise moments $= 400 \text{ N} \times 0.6 \text{ m}$,
anticlockwise moments $= \text{effort} \times 1.5 \text{ m}$.
In equilibrium, clockwise moments = anticlockwise moments,
$$400 \times 0.6 \, (\text{N m}) = \text{effort} \times 1.5 \, (\text{N m})$$
$$\text{effort} = \frac{400 \times 0.6}{1.5}$$
$$\text{effort} = \frac{240}{1.5}$$
$$= 160 \text{ N}.$$

Therefore, an effort of just over 160 newtons is required to move the load
(160 N alone just balances the load).

$$\text{Mechanical advantage} = \frac{\text{load}}{\text{effort}} = \frac{400 \text{ N}}{160 \text{ N}}$$
$$= \frac{40}{16} = \frac{10}{4} = 2.5.$$

☐ **Toggles**

Toggle clamps are used to obtain large clamping forces. The mechanism
consists of two links on a common pivot. The free end of one link is pivoted to a
fixed surface (Fig. 1.18). The free end of the second lever is constrained to move
in a straight line. By applying a horizontal effort to the common pivot, the
lower end of the toggle mechanism is pushed downwards. The effort is usually

16

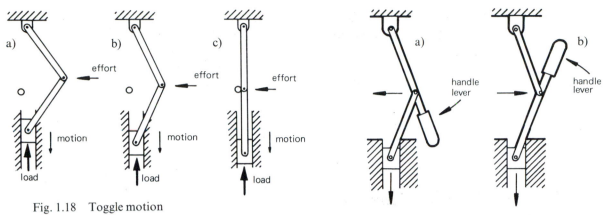

Fig. 1.18   Toggle motion

Fig. 1.19   Applying the toggle force

applied by a handle (Fig. 1.19). The maximum clamping force occurs when the links are in a straight line. Thus the toggle clamp is made up of a lever and a link. Cams, screws or pneumatic cylinders can be used to apply the effort.

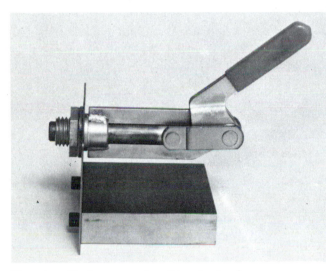

Fig. 1.20   The Brauer push-pull toggle clamp

Fig. 1.21   The Brauer vertical toggle clamp

Industry makes considerable use of toggle clamps (Figs. 1.20 and 1.21) to secure work being machined, pressed or formed. Figure 1.22 shows a drilling jig where a small toggle clamp secures the workpiece.

17

Toggle clamps can be used in a school workshop to hold work being drilled or to hold hot plastic sheet on vacuum forming machines or on blow moulding machines.

The toggle principle is used on prams and push chairs to create tension and retain the hood when in use.

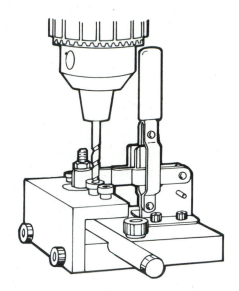

Fig. 1.22   A drilling jig using a toggle clamp

■ Linkages

It is often convenient to think of a mechanism as a 'black box'. It is not important what goes on inside the 'black box', just what needs to go into it to produce the output you want. Thus the 'black box' might be a linkage mechanism of some sort.

Fig. 1.23   A 'black box' mechanism

The system inside the 'black box' alters the input motion in some desired way. For example, it might reverse the motion or turn the motion through a right angle or change linear motion into rotary motion (Fig. 1.24).

Fig. 1.24   'Black box' functions

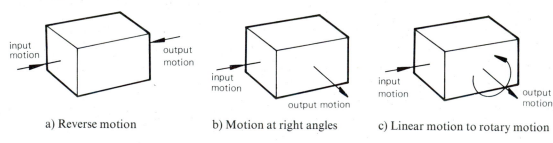

a) Reverse motion   b) Motion at right angles   c) Linear motion to rotary motion

We have already looked at the possible contents of such 'black boxes'. Later we will see how individual 'black box' mechanisms can be connected together to make complex mechanisms and machines.

18

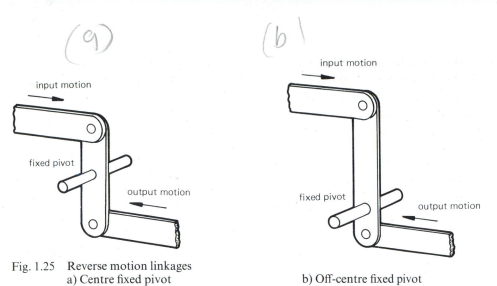

Fig. 1.25   Reverse motion linkages
           a) Centre fixed pivot   b) Off-centre fixed pivot

One type of 'black box' function is created by an assembly of levers which transforms and transmits an input. This assembly is called a linkage. A single lever with a pivot at its centre reverses an input motion (Fig. 1.25a). A lever with its pivot at the centre does not affect the input force. If the pivot is not at the mid-point of the lever (Fig. 1.25b), the input force is increased or decreased at the output according to the position of the pivot. The reverse rotary motion shown in Fig. 1.26 is a variation of the simple reverse motion linkage.

Fig. 1.26   A rotary linkage

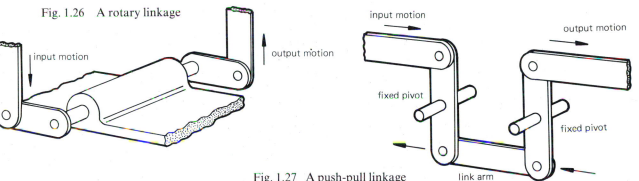

Fig. 1.27   A push-pull linkage

To achieve an output motion in the same direction as the input motion, a push-pull linkage can be used (Fig. 1.27). Two fixed pivots and an extra link arm are necessary.

Fig. 1.28   An equalising linkage

An equalising linkage (Fig. 1.28) is used when it is necessary to divide the applied input force along two output links, for example when motion and force need to be transferred from one hydraulic or pneumatic cylinder to two brakes or clutches.

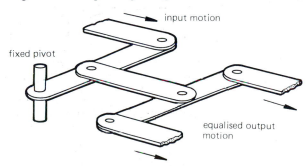

19

Linkages are used in school workshops to transmit the force required to operate bench shears, a press or a punch tool. A simple press using linkages could be made in the workshop for pressing bearings on to shafts or removing bearings from their housings. The same linkage could be used to operate a punch tool that would produce shapes in thin metal sheet, perhaps for use in a piece of jewellery. An example of such a linkage is shown in Fig. 1.29.

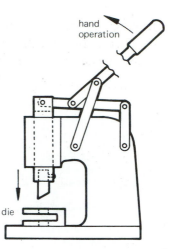

Fig. 1.29   A linkage for a jewellery press

■ **Parallel Motion Linkages**

If four Meccano strips are connected with loose nut and bolt joints as shown in Fig. 1.30a, the result is a **parallel linkage**. The two long Meccano strips or links are parallel as are the two shorter strips or links. In Fig. 1.30b, if a load is applied to link *CD* the whole mechanism moves but links *CD* and *AB* are still parallel. Links *AD* and *BC* are also still parallel. Further, if an input motion is applied to link *AD*, it produces an identical output motion at link *BC*.

Fig. 1.30   a) A parallel linkage   b) Links remain parallel

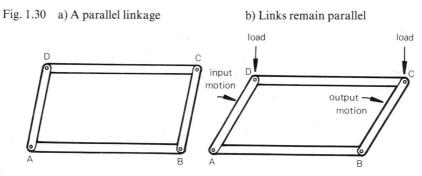

Examples of parallel linkages are found in the trammels used by draughtsmen for drawing parallel lines and in the parallel hinges used on tool and needlework boxes (Fig. 1.31).

Fig. 1.31   a) Parallel trammels   b) Parallel hinges on a tool box

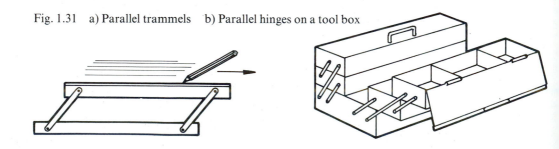

20

Another drawing instrument that makes use of the parallel linkage is the pantograph. This is used to enlarge or reduce a drawing. The drawing and the copy are similar in shape but differ in scale (Fig. 1.32a).

Fig. 1.32   a) The pantograph linkage   b) The lazy-tongs linkage

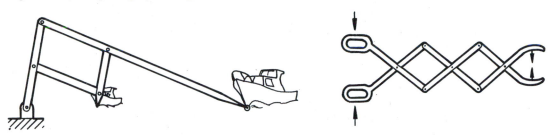

Lazy-tongs (Fig. 1.32b) use the parallel linkage principle. The lazy-tongs are used for picking up objects which are dangerous or inaccessible.

□ **Graphic Symbols**

Very complex mechanisms and linkages consist of basically simple devices. For example, a typewriter mechanism (Fig. 1.33) can be seen to be made up of a series of simple levers.

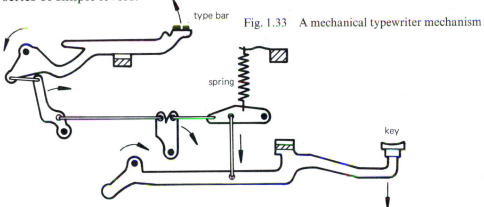

Fig. 1.33   A mechanical typewriter mechanism

Drawing complex mechanisms such as this is a time-consuming and difficult job. However, the functioning of a mechanical system can be easily illustrated by the use of graphic symbols for levers, pivots and springs. Figure 1.34 shows some graphic symbols which can be used to simplify the drawing of a complex mechanism.

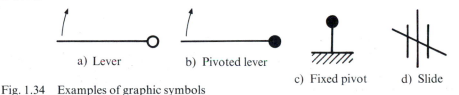

a) Lever   b) Pivoted lever   c) Fixed pivot   d) Slide

Fig. 1.34   Examples of graphic symbols

21

Figure 1.35 shows graphic symbols used to represent the typewriter mechanism shown in Fig. 1.33.

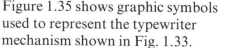

Fig. 1.35   The typewriter mechanism using graphic symbols

■ Construction Kits

MECCANO CONSTRUCTION KIT

The most useful Meccano parts for building mechanisms of levers or linkages are perforated strips (Fig. 1.36a) with nuts and bolts used for joint pivots. Axle rods can also form pivots when used with perforated strips.

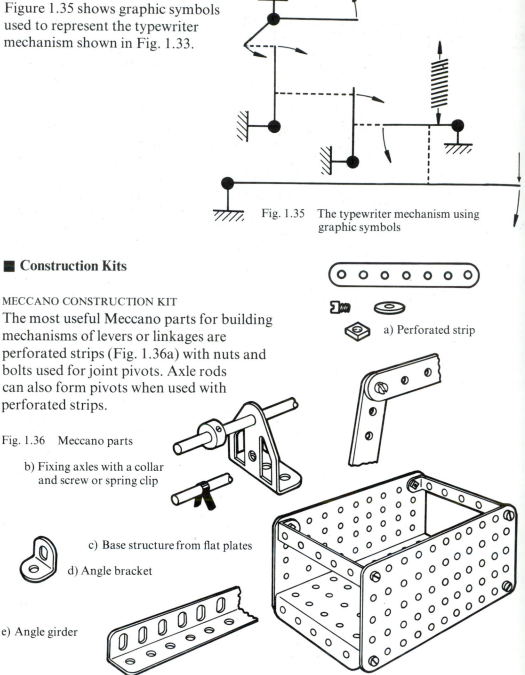

a) Perforated strip

Fig. 1.36   Meccano parts

b) Fixing axles with a collar and screw or spring clip

c) Base structure from flat plates

d) Angle bracket

e) Angle girder

Axle rods are fixed with a collar and screw or a spring clip (Fig. 1.36b). Simple structures to support a mechanism are best built with flat plates as a base and sides. They are secured with double angle strips (Fig. 1.36c).

22

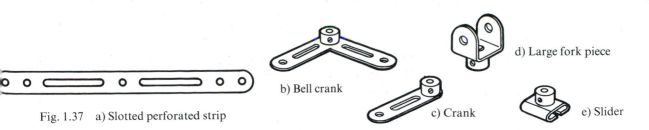

Fig. 1.37   a) Slotted perforated strip
b) Bell crank
c) Crank
d) Large fork piece
e) Slider

Rigid structures to support mechanisms can be made with flat plates and angle brackets (Fig. 1.36d) or angle girders (Fig. 1.36e). Other Meccano components which can be used for constructing linkages are shown in Fig. 1.37.

FISCHERTECHNIK CONSTRUCTION KIT

The Fischertechnik construction system uses building blocks which are fastened together by lugs on the end of each block. These fit into keyway slots. Long links or levers can be constructed by fitting one block on top of another (Fig. 1.38a and b). Elbow joints can be used to make a hinge joint (Fig. 1.38c). Pivot fixings can be made with axles (Fig. 1.38d). Small building blocks with a red lug at the end will rotate, and can be used as a pivot fixing (Fig. 1.38e). Simple structures are best built on a flat base plate (Fig. 1.38f). Angled structures can be built with the aid of an angle block (Fig. 1.38g).

Fig. 1.38   Fischertechnik components

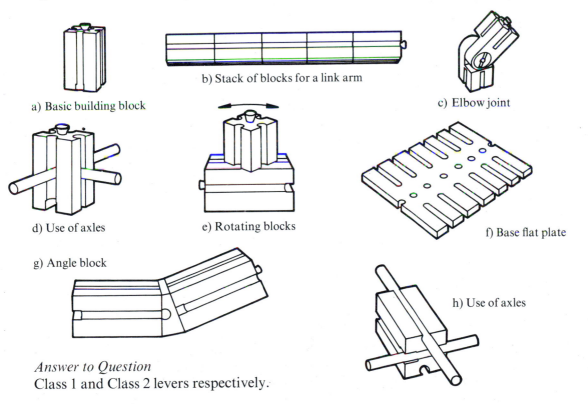

a) Basic building block
b) Stack of blocks for a link arm
c) Elbow joint
d) Use of axles
e) Rotating blocks
f) Base flat plate
g) Angle block
h) Use of axles

Answer to Question
Class 1 and Class 2 levers respectively.

2 Pulleys and Sprockets

■ Introduction to Pulleys

Rotary motion is the most common type of motion for a shaft or an axle.

1 What is the graphic symbol used to indicate 'rotary motion'?
2 What units are used to measure rotary motion?

One way in which an engineer uses rotary motion is by transmitting it from one shaft to another when the shafts are parallel (Fig. 2.1a). This can be done by using pulleys and belts (Fig. 2.1b). A **pulley** is a wheel with a grooved rim.

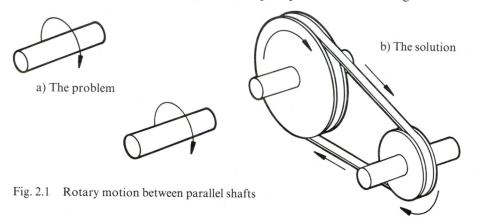

a) The problem

b) The solution

Fig. 2.1   Rotary motion between parallel shafts

3 In Fig. 2.1b, what have the motions of the two shafts in common?
Note that the linear motion of the belt between the two pulleys is in two opposite directions.

4 What effect on linear motion has a single pulley (Fig. 2.2)?

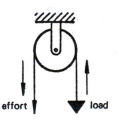

Fig. 2.2   A single pulley

effort   load

A crossed belt is used between two pulleys when the parallel shafts are required to turn in opposite directions. Notice that, because the belt crosses, it is necessary to offset the alignment of the pulleys on their shafts (Fig. 2.3b).

Graphic symbols can be used to represent pulleys and a belt (Fig. 2.4a and b).

24

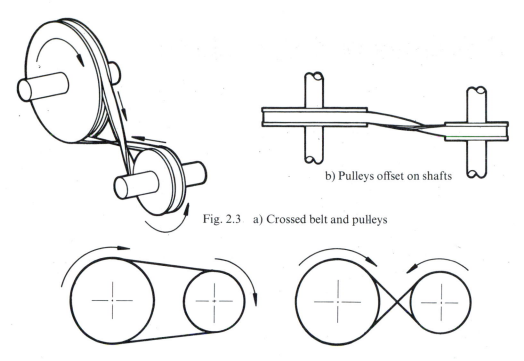

b) Pulleys offset on shafts

Fig. 2.3   a) Crossed belt and pulleys

Fig. 2.4   a) Graphic symbol of pulleys and belt   b) Graphic symbol of crossed belt and pulleys

5   *Name some machines which you have seen at home or in the school workshop that use a pulley and belt mechanism.*

■ Input and Output Velocities of Rotation

Belt and pulley systems are often used where an electric motor has to drive a machine. The pulley on the motor is called the **driver pulley**. The pulley on the machine being driven by the belt is called a **driven pulley**. This can be illustrated on a rumble mill, a device for polishing semi-precious stones used in jewellery work (Fig. 2.5).

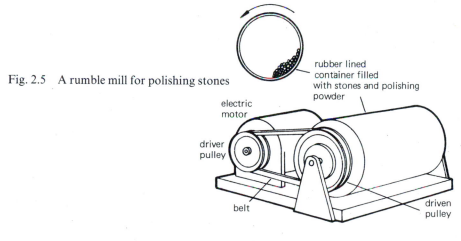

Fig. 2.5   A rumble mill for polishing stones

rubber lined container filled with stones and polishing powder

electric motor

driver pulley

belt

driven pulley

6 *A motor car fan belt is used to rotate the cooling fan and generator (or alternator). The fan belt is turned by a pulley attached to the engine crankshaft. Which is the driver and which is the driven pulley. (Fig. 2.6)?*

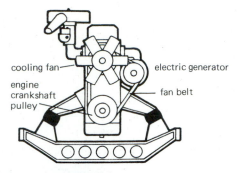

Fig. 2.6 The fan belt on a motor car

When a machine is being driven by a pulley and belt system, the velocity of rotation of the machine shaft is determined by a) the velocity of rotation of the driving motor and b) the size of the pulleys. Consider the diagram in Fig. 2.7.

Fig. 2.7 Pulley and belt driving systems

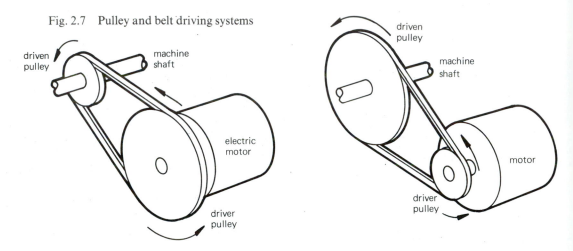

a) Rotary velocity increase

b) Rotary velocity reduction

When the motor driver pulley has a large diameter and the machine shaft driven pulley has a small diameter, the machine shaft goes faster than the motor shaft. There is an increase in rotary velocity (Fig. 2.7a). If a small diameter pulley is attached to the driver motor and a large diameter pulley is attached to the driven machine shaft, there is a reduction in rotary velocity (Fig. 2.7b).

An electric motor applies an effort to a driver pulley. The distance moved by the effort is the input motion. The distance moved by the load is the output motion. Suppose a pulley of diameter 40 mm uses a belt to drive a pulley of diameter 20 mm (Fig. 2.8). The driver pulley is twice the diameter of the driven pulley. When the driver pulley turns one revolution, the driven pulley rotates two revolutions.

26

Fig. 2.8   A pulley and belt system

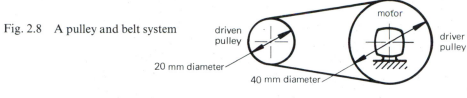

As velocity ratio = $\dfrac{\text{distance moved by effort (input movement)}}{\text{distance moved by load (output movement)}}$

the velocity ratio of this pulley system

$$= \dfrac{\text{distance moved by driver pulley}}{\text{distance moved by the driven pulley}}$$

$$= \dfrac{1 \text{ revolution}}{2 \text{ revolutions}}.$$

Therefore, velocity ratio $= \frac{1}{2}$.

As this is usually written as a ratio, the velocity ratio is $1:2$.
If the rotary velocity of one shaft is known the rotary velocity of the other shaft can be calculated.

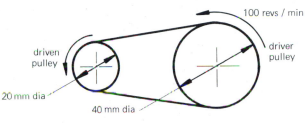

Example
Suppose a motor pulley has a diameter of 40 mm and it is driving a machine pulley of diameter 20 mm (Fig. 2.9). If the motor driver pulley rotates at 100 revs/min, what is the rotary velocity of the driven machine pulley?

Fig. 2.9   The rotary velocity of driver and driven shafts

When the driver motor pulley rotates one revolution, the driven pulley rotates two revolutions. Therefore the driven pulley must have twice the rotary velocity of the driver pulley. As the rotary velocity of the driver pulley shaft is 100 revs/min, the rotary velocity of the driven pulley shaft is 200 revs/min.

$$\text{Velocity ratio} = \dfrac{\text{distance moved by driver pulley}}{\text{distance moved by driven pulley}} = \dfrac{1 \text{ rev}}{2 \text{ rev}} = \dfrac{1}{2}$$

$$= \dfrac{\text{rotary velocity of driver pulley}}{\text{rotary velocity of driven pulley}} = \dfrac{100 \text{ revs/min}}{200 \text{ revs/min}} = \dfrac{1}{2}$$

$$= \dfrac{\text{diameter of driven pulley}}{\text{diameter of driver pulley}} = \dfrac{20 \text{ mm}}{40 \text{ mm}} = \dfrac{1}{2}.$$

Pulley shaft rotary velocities can be calculated from the formula:

rotary velocity of driven pulley × diameter of driven pulley =
rotary velocity of driver pulley × diameter of driver pulley.

Therefore, rotary velocity of driven pulley =

$$\dfrac{\text{rotary velocity of driver pulley} \times \text{diameter of driver pulley}}{\text{diameter of driven pulley}}.$$

In this example,

$$\text{rotary velocity of driven pulley} = \frac{100 \text{ revs/min} \times 40 \text{ mm}}{20 \text{ mm}} = \frac{100 \times 40}{20}.$$

Therefore, velocity of driven pulley = 200 revs/min.

Example

A 30 mm diameter driver pulley is attached to an electric motor which rotates at 450 revs/min (Fig. 2.10). By means of a belt, the motor drives a driven pulley of 90 mm diameter. What is the rotary velocity of the driven pulley shaft?

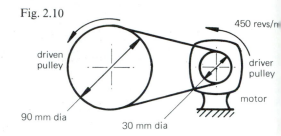

Fig. 2.10

450 revs/m

driven pulley

driver pulley

motor

90 mm dia

30 mm dia

Rotary velocity of driven pulley

$$= \frac{\text{rotary velocity of driver pulley} \times \text{diameter of driver pulley}}{\text{diameter of driven pulley}}$$

$$= \frac{450 \times 30}{90} \text{ revs/min}.$$

Therefore, rotary velocity of driven pulley = 150 revs/min.

■ Pulley and Belt Types and Applications

The main functions of pulley and belt systems are to transmit motion and torque from an engine to a machine. Various types of pulley and belt are used on different machines. Machines used in the home, such as sewing machines, washing machines, spin driers and upright vacuum cleaners, often use round **grooved pulleys** and **round belts** made from rubber. A grooved pulley can be secured to its shaft by a threaded grub screw (Fig. 2.11).

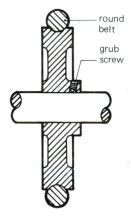

round belt

grub screw

Fig. 2.11   A section through a grooved pulley and round belt

Machine tools, such as drilling machines, lathes and milling machines, are usually driven by **vee pulleys** and **vee belts** (Fig. 2.12a). A section through a vee pulley, shown in Fig. 2.12b, indicates how the vee pulley is 'keyed' to the driving shaft. A keyway groove is cut in both the pulley and the driving shaft. The pulley is secured by a tapered key. The mass of the pulley is reduced by a web section between the vee rim and the centre boss.

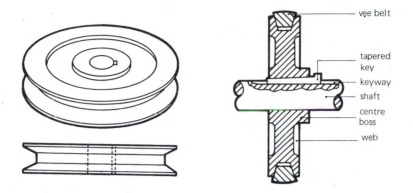

Fig. 2.12   a) The vee pulley   b) A section through a vee pulley and vee belt

When large torques have to be transmitted between shafts, stacked pulleys are used with several driving belts (Fig. 2.13).

Fig. 2.13   Stacked vee pulleys and vee belts

7   *Why do you think vee belts are better than round belts for driving large machines?*

On some machine tools, such as drilling machines, it is necessary to provide a range of shaft speeds. This is achieved by stepped cone pulleys as shown in Fig. 2.14.

Fig. 2.14   Stepped cone pulleys provide a range of shaft speeds

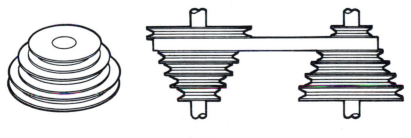

Fig. 2.15   Flat belt drive from a heat engine

In the past, **flat pulleys** and flat belts were often used to transmit torque and motion from engines to machines (Fig. 2.15). The **flat belt** was usually made from woven cord or leather. Flat pulleys (Fig. 2.16) were usually made of cast iron.

The pulley had several spokes, rather than a web, to reduce its mass and hence make it lighter and easier to support on its axle. Notice that the 'flat' pulley is slightly barrel-shaped. This 'crowned' effect helps to keep the flat belt riding centrally on the pulley.

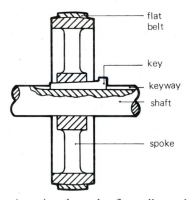

Fig. 2.16   A section through a flat pulley and flat belt

Many agricultural machines, which were driven by traction engines, used flat pulleys and belts to transmit motion and torque. Fig. 2.17 shows a threshing machine which was driven by a traction engine using flat belts and pulleys.

30

Fig. 2.17   A threshing machine – an example of the use of flat belts and pulleys

8   *If a pulley belt is slightly loose as shown in Fig. 2.18, what major problem is likely to arise when it is used to drive a machine?*

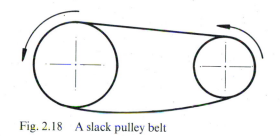

Fig. 2.18   A slack pulley belt

Fig. 2.19   The use of a jockey pulley

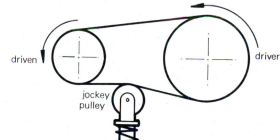

A method of avoiding slip in a pulley and belt system is to keep the belt taut by means of a **jockey pulley**. A jockey pulley is shown in Fig. 2.19. It is an additional pulley which keeps the maximum amount of belt in contact with the driver and driven pulleys. The jockey pulley is often spring loaded.

Belt slip in pulley systems can be an advantage. If a machine tool jams or seizes and the belt slips on the pulleys, the driving motor is unlikely to be overloaded and damaged. In machines where a positive drive is essential and

31

Fig. 2.20   Toothed belt and pulleys

no slip between belt and pulleys can be accepted, a toothed belt and pulley is used. A **toothed belt and pulley** is shown in Fig. 2.20. Toothed belts are mainly used for timing mechanisms, where a quiet, positive (no slip) drive is required, such as driving a camshaft in a motor car engine.

■ Sprockets and Chains

Where it is a disadvantage to have belt slip a toothed wheel, called a **sprocket**, and a chain can be used.
A **chain** consists of many loosely jointed links (Fig. 2.21).

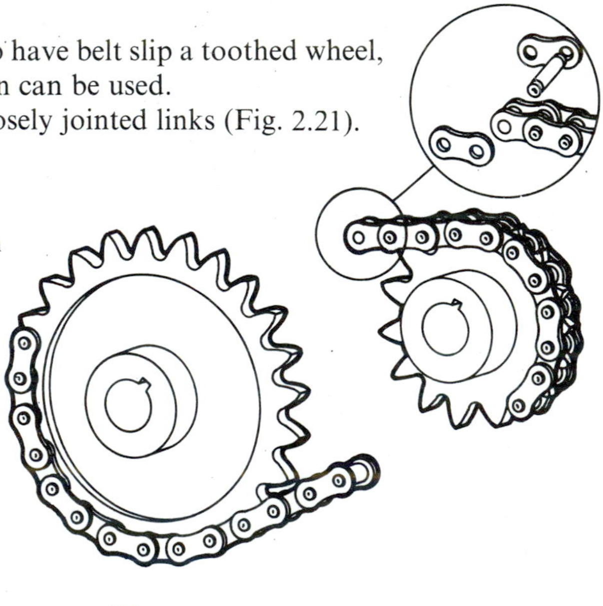

Fig. 2.21   Sprockets and chain

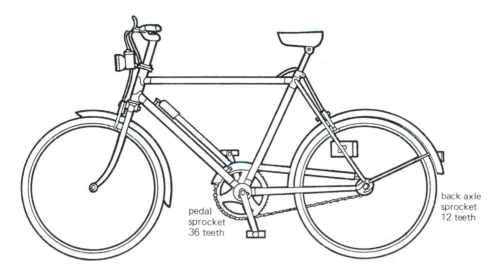

pedal
sprocket
36 teeth

back axle
sprocket
12 teeth

Fig. 2.22   A bicycle chain and sprockets

Sprockets and chains are used when a direct positive drive is essential, for example on a bicycle (Fig. 2.22).

Fig. 2.23   Chain drive on a kart – engine to rear axle (chain guard removed)

Sprockets and chains are also used on motorcycles and karts (Fig. 2.23).

As it is difficult and tedious to draw the teeth of a sprocket and the links of a chain, graphic symbols can be used to represent them (Fig. 2.24).

Fig. 2.24   Graphic symbol of sprockets and chain

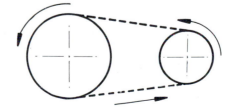

The links of a chain require equal spacing of equal teeth on the driver and driven sprockets. Because of this, the velocity ratio of a sprocket and chain mechanism is determined by the number of teeth on each sprocket.

$$\text{Velocity ratio} = \frac{\text{number of teeth on driven sprocket}}{\text{number of teeth on driver sprocket}}.$$

Example

The bicycle shown in Fig. 2.22 has a driver sprocket (pedal sprocket) with 36 teeth and a driven sprocket (back wheel sprocket) with 12 teeth. If the pedal sprocket is rotated through one revolution, how many times does the back wheel go round? What is the velocity ratio of the sprocket and chain mechanism?

If the driver sprocket turns one revolution, then 36 teeth mesh with the chain in one revolution. Since the driver sprocket and the driven sprocket are connected with chain, 36 teeth on the driven sprocket must mesh with the chain. But there are only 12 teeth on the driven sprocket. Therefore the driven sprocket (and hence the back wheel) must rotate three times for every one revolution of the driver sprocket ($3 \times 12 = 36$).

$$\text{Velocity ratio} = \frac{\text{number of teeth on driven sprocket}}{\text{number of teeth on driver sprocket}}$$

$$= \frac{12}{36} = \frac{1}{3}.$$

Therefore, velocity ratio $= 1:3$.

The rotary velocities of sprocket shafts can be calculated from the formula:

rotary velocity of driven sprocket shaft =

$$\frac{\text{rotary velocity of driver sprocket shaft} \times \text{number of teeth on driver sprocket}}{\text{number of teeth on driven sprocket}}$$

Example

The engine sprocket of a kart has 9 teeth and the back axle sprocket has 72 teeth. If the engine rotates at 4800 revs/min, what is the rotary velocity of the back axle?

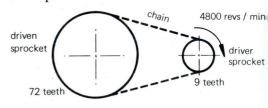

Fig. 2.25 Sprocket and chain mechanism for a kart

Rotary velocity of back axle

$$= \frac{\text{rotary velocity of driver sprocket} \times \text{number of teeth on driver sprocket}}{\text{number of teeth on driven sprocket}}$$

$$= \frac{4800 \times 9}{72} = \frac{4800}{8} \text{ revs/min.}$$

Therefore, rotary velocity of back axle $= 600$ revs/min.

Fig. 2.26 shows an industrial use of pulleys and belts and sprockets and chains. The guards have been removed so that the mechanism can be seen.

On moving machinery, pulleys and belt mechanisms and sprockets and chain mechanisms should always be guarded. Do not approach unguarded moving mechanisms.

Fig. 2.26   The need for guards on moving belts and chains

■ Construction Kits

MECCANO

In the Meccano range of components there are two kinds of pulleys:
(a) freely revolving pulleys (Fig. 2.27) which can be used to change the direction of action of a tension force or in lifting devices;
(b) pulleys with a central boss and a grub screw to key them to a shaft (Fig. 2.28)
Meccano pulleys range in diameter from 12 mm to 75 mm.

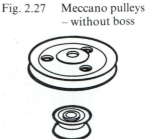

Fig. 2.27   Meccano pulleys
            – without boss

Fig. 2.28   Meccano pulleys   – with boss

Meccano sprockets range from 14 teeth to 56 teeth. A sprocket and sprocket chain are shown in Fig. 2.29.

Fig. 2.29   a) A sprocket   b) A sprocket chain

FISCHERTECHNIK

A range of plastic pulleys is available in the Fischertechnik kit (Fig. 2.30).

Fig. 2.30   Fischertechnik pulleys

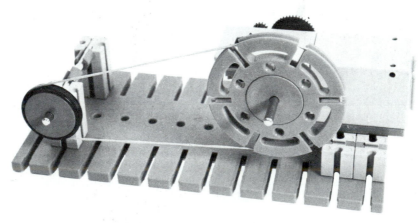

A large tyre and hub can be used as a pulley (Fig. 2.31).

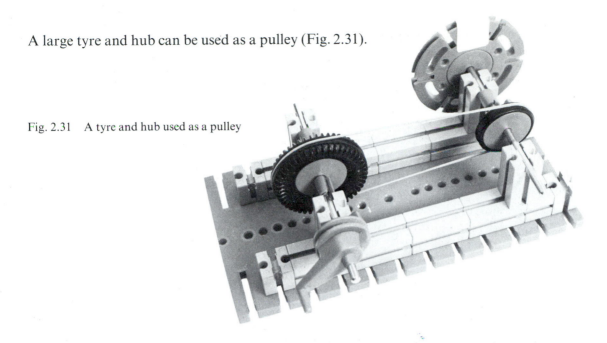

Fig. 2.31   A tyre and hub used as a pulley

Two Fischertechnik pulley and belt mechanisms are shown in Fig. 2.32. The Fischertechnik sprocket chain is shown in Fig. 2.34. Sprockets are not available as a separate item, and so gears are used as sprockets. A typical sprocket and chain mechanism is shown in Fig. 2.33.

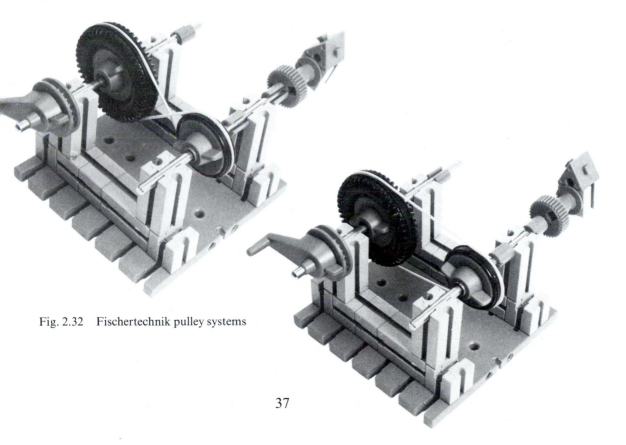

Fig. 2.32   Fischertechnik pulley systems

Fig. 2.33   Fischertechnik gear sprocket and chain

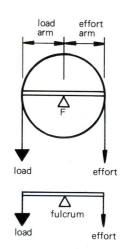

Fig. 2.34   Fischertechnik

■ Pulleys and Lifting Devices

The pulley is a form of Class 1 lever (Fig. 2.35). It has a load arm the same length as the effort arm. The length of each arm is the radius of the pulley.

When a single pulley is used as a lifting device (Fig. 2.36) its only function is to change the direction of the tension force (T) in the rope. When an equal load force and effort force are applied to the pulley system, the pulley will be at rest. The pulley system is said to be in equilibrium under the action of the two equal forces. The load only starts to rise when a larger effort force is applied. Machines of this kind are used on building sites to lift bricks, because it is easier to apply an effort downwards rather than upwards.

Fig. 2.35   The pulley as a lever

Fig. 2.36   A single pulley

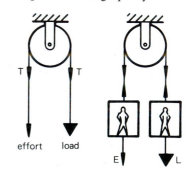

38

The mechanical advantage of this pulley system $= \dfrac{\text{load}}{\text{effort}}$.

Since the load and effort are equal, the mechanical advantage is 1. There is no mechanical advantage from a single pulley.

9   *What is the velocity ratio of this pulley system?*

Mechanical advantage can be gained if the single pulley is able to move. The load is hung on the pulley block (Fig. 2.37). This is really the system shown in Fig. 2.35 turned upside down. The load is now supported equally by the part of the rope to the right and the part of the rope to the left of the pulley. The tension force in the left part of the rope is half the load force. As the effort force equals the tension force, it too is half the load force. Looking at it another way, if the original effort is applied, twice the previous load can be raised.

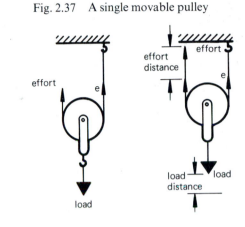

Fig. 2.37   A single movable pulley

Mechanical advantage $= \dfrac{\text{load}}{\text{effort}} = \dfrac{2}{1}$.

Therefore the mechanical advantage is 2.

If the load is to be raised 1 metre, each half of the rope has to be shortened by 1 metre. Therefore, the effort has had to move twice as far as the load.

Velocity ratio $= \dfrac{\text{distance moved by effort}}{\text{distance moved by load}} = \dfrac{2}{1}$.

Therefore, the velocity ratio is 2.

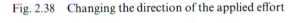

Fig. 2.38   Changing the direction of the applied effort

10   *It is awkward to apply an effort force in an upwards direction. How can the direction of the applied effort be changed?*

The fixed single pulley and the movable pulley are often combined as one lifting device as shown in Fig. 2.39. The mechanical advantage and the velocity ratio of the combined pulley are still both equal to 2 in this system.

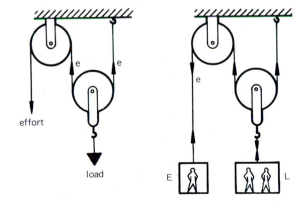

11 *If the combined pulley block shown in Fig. 2.39 was used to lift a load of 20 newtons, what effort would be required?*

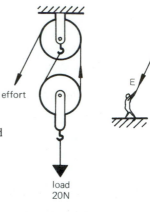

effort

Fig. 2.39   A combined fixed and movable pulley

load
20N

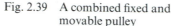

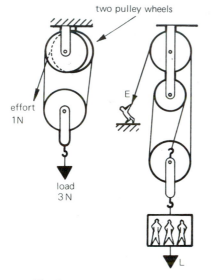

two pulley wheels

effort
1N

E

load
3 N

Fig. 2.40   A three pulley wheel lifting device

L

The lifting device shown in Fig. 2.40 consists of a single rope and three pulleys. The pulley block has two pulleys free to rotate about a fixed axis at the top, and one lower movable pulley. The pulleys divide the rope into three parts, and each part supports $\frac{1}{3}$ of the load.

$$\text{Effort} = \frac{\text{load}}{3}.$$

$$\text{Mechanical advantage} = \frac{\text{load}}{\text{effort}} = \frac{\text{load}}{\text{load}/3} = 3.$$

$$\text{Velocity ratio} = \frac{\text{distance moved by effort}}{\text{distance moved by load}}$$

$$= \frac{3}{1} = 3.$$

The lifting device shown in Fig. 2.41 has four pulleys and a single rope. It has two blocks consisting of two pulleys free to rotate about their axles. The upper block is fixed and the lower pulley block is movable. Although the pulleys in each block are shown one beneath the other, in practice they are on the same axle. The pulleys divide the rope into four parts, and each part supports $\frac{1}{4}$ of the load.

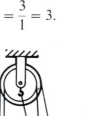

1N
effort

4 N
load

Fig. 2.41   A lifting system using four pulleys

load

40

$$\text{Effort} = \frac{\text{load}}{4}.$$

$$\text{Mechanical advantage} = \frac{\text{load}}{\text{effort}} = \frac{4}{1} = 4.$$

$$\text{Velocity ratio} = \frac{\text{distance moved by effort}}{\text{distance moved by load}}$$

$$= \frac{4}{1} = 4.$$

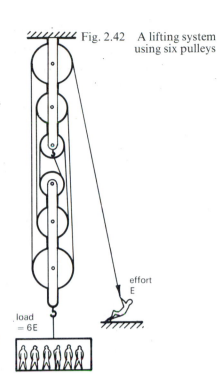

Fig. 2.42   A lifting system using six pulleys

The lifting device shown in Fig. 2.42 has six pulleys which divide the rope into six parts. Each part supports $\frac{1}{6}$ of the load. The system therefore has a mechanical advantage of 6 and also a velocity ratio of 6.

Figure 2.43 shows a pulley system which uses more than one rope. Each half of rope A supports half the load. The right-hand half of rope A applies this force to pulley B. Each half of rope B supports half of this force, half of half the load, i.e. load/4.

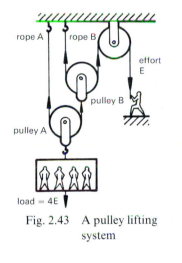

Fig. 2.43   A pulley lifting system

$$\text{Effort} = \frac{\text{load}}{4}.$$

$$\text{Mechanical advantage} = \frac{\text{load}}{\text{effort}} = \frac{\text{load}}{\text{load}/4} = 4.$$

$$\text{Velocity ratio} = \frac{\text{distance moved by effort}}{\text{distance moved by load}} = \frac{4}{1} = 4.$$

12   *Draw a pulley system similar to that in Fig. 2.43 but having one more rope and one more pulley. What is the mechanical advantage and velocity ratio of the new system?*

13   *Can you think of applications where pulleys are used for lifting?*

☐ The Wheel and Axle

The **wheel and axle** provides a mechanical advantage by use of a large radius wheel and a smaller radius axle. The wheel and the axle are fixed together rigidly. Examples of a wheel and axle system are the shaft and wheel of a motor car, bicycle wheel and axle, car steering wheel, train wheel and axle, a gear wheel and shaft. The wheel can be regarded as a large rotating lever (Fig. 2.44b) which is fixed to a smaller rotating lever, the axle.

Fig. 2.44

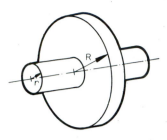

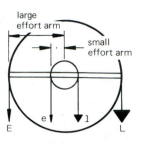

a) The wheel and axle principle   b) A wheel and axle as a lever

Fig. 2.45   Wheel and axle (windlass)

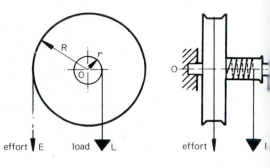

Earlier we saw how this mechanism was used in a windlass to lift heavy weights. The windlass shown in Fig. 2.45 consists of a large wheel, radius R, and an axle, radius r. A rope attached to a load is wound round the axle. A second rope is wound round the large wheel. By pulling on the rope round the large wheel, a man is able to lift a heavy weight because of the mechanical advantage gained.

The mechanical advantage is found by taking moments about the pivot axis O.
   In equilibrium, clockwise moments equal anticlockwise moments, therefore

$$\text{effort} \times R = \text{load} \times r,$$
$$\frac{\text{load}}{\text{effort}} = \frac{R}{r}.$$

$$\text{Mechanical advantage} = \frac{\text{load}}{\text{effort}} = \frac{R}{r}$$
$$= \frac{\text{radius of effort wheel}}{\text{radius of load axle}}.$$

Therefore mechanical advantage $= \dfrac{R}{r}$.

Velocity ratio is the ratio of the circumferences of the wheel and the axle.

$$\text{Velocity ratio} = \frac{\text{distance moved by effort}}{\text{distance moved by load}}$$
$$= \frac{\text{circumference of wheel}}{\text{circumference of axle}}$$
$$= \frac{2\pi R}{2\pi r}$$

Therefore velocity ratio $= \dfrac{R}{r}$.

☐ The Weston Differential Pulley

A Weston differential pulley block can be used to lift a very heavy weight, for example lifting the engine out of a car. It consists of a continuous rope or chain round two upper pulleys and one lower movable pulley. The two top pulleys have different diameters but they are rigidly connected together. Toothed pulleys are often used with a continuous chain rather than a rope. This has the advantage of removing the possibility of a rope slipping on a pulley when under heavy load.
The special advantage of the Weston differential pulley is that the effort will move the load but the load cannot move the effort. It will not run in reverse like other pulley systems.

The mechanical advantage is calculated by taking moments about the pivot axle of the top pulley block:

in equilibrium, effort $\times R = \left(\dfrac{\text{load}}{2} \times R\right) - \left(\dfrac{\text{load}}{2} \times r\right)$

(where R is the radius of the large pulley and r is the radius of the small pulley)

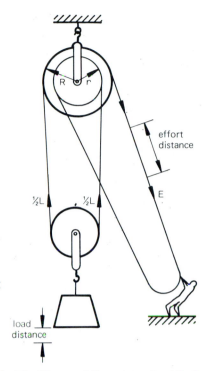

Fig. 2.46   The Weston differential pulley block

$$\text{effort} \times R = \frac{\text{load}}{2}(R-r)$$

$\dfrac{\text{load}}{\text{effort}} = \dfrac{2R}{(R-r)}$. Therefore the mechanical advantage $= \dfrac{2R}{(R-r)}$.

Velocity ratio can be calculated by considering how much the loop is shortened in one revolution of the large pulley. When the large pulley is rotated, the rope winds up on the larger pulley and unwinds from the smaller pulley. The rope is shortened by the difference between the circumferences of the two pulleys. The load is raised half the difference between the circumferences. In one revolution of the large pulley, the loop in the rope is shortened by $2\pi(R-r)$. Therefore the load is raised $\pi(R-r)$.
   In one revolution of the large pulley, the effort is applied through a distance of $2\pi R$.

Velocity ratio $= \dfrac{\text{distance moved by effort}}{\text{distance moved by load}} = \dfrac{2\pi R}{\pi(R-r)}$

Therefore velocity ratio $= \dfrac{2R}{(R-r)}$.

43

■ Torque

The turning effect of a belt on a pulley is called the **torque**. The torque on a pulley is found as follows (Fig. 2.47):

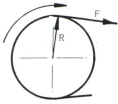

Fig. 2.47   Torque

torque = turning force × pulley radius = $F \times R$.

Force is measured in newtons (N). The pulley radius is measured in metres (m). Therefore, torque is measured in newton metres (N m).

When a motor is providing a turning force, this is called the motor torque. A motor turning a drum to wind up a rope (Fig. 2.48) produces a motor torque of $F \times r$.

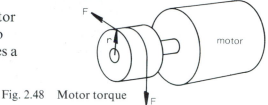

Fig. 2.48   Motor torque

When a pulley is driven by a belt (Fig. 2.49) the top part of the belt is tighter than the bottom part. If the larger (top) tension force is F_1 and the smaller (bottom) tension force is F_2 (Fig. 2.50), the torque on the pulley is $R(F_1 - F_2)$.
Torque = $R(F_1 - F_2)$.

Fig. 2.49   Tension forces in a belt

Fig. 2.50   Torque on a belt-driven pulley

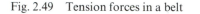

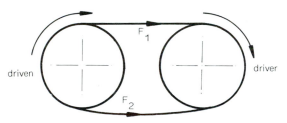

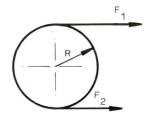

■ The Efficiency of Machines

Pulley lifting systems enable heavy loads to be moved with a small effort. In calculating the effort required to move a load we made an assumption that ropes and pulleys have no weight and that the pulley bearings are frictionless. In reality, a small amount of extra effort is needed to move this weight and overcome the friction forces.

A machine that moves a load through a distance is doing 'work'.

14   What is the formula for calculating 'work'?

In a real machine more work is done by the effort than is done by the machine. More work (or energy) is put in than is got out. The **efficiency** of a machine is the ratio of the useful output of work to the total input of work.

$$\text{Efficiency} = \frac{\text{work out}}{\text{work in}} \times 100\% \text{ (Efficiency is usually given as a percentage.)}$$

But work = force × distance,

therefore,

$$\text{efficiency} = \frac{\text{load} \times \text{distance moved by the load}}{\text{effort} \times \text{distance moved by the effort}} \times 100\%.$$

Study this equation carefully. It can be seen that efficiency can be expressed in terms of mechanical advantage and velocity ratio:

$$\text{mechanical advantage} = \frac{\text{load}}{\text{effort}}$$

$$\text{and velocity ratio} = \frac{\text{distance moved by effort}}{\text{distance moved by load}}.$$

$$\text{Therefore, efficiency} = \frac{\text{mechanical advantage}}{\text{velocity ratio}} \times 100\%.$$

Example 1
A pulley system is shown in Fig. 2.51.
An effort of 15 N moves a load of
30 N. The effort moves through 1
metre when the load moves through
0.5 metres. Assume the ropes and
pulleys are weightless and the pulleys
are frictionless. Calculate the efficiency
of the system.

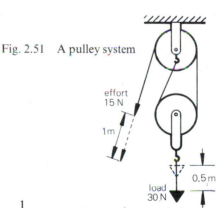

Fig. 2.51   A pulley system

effort
15 N

1 m

load
30 N

0.5 m

$$\text{Mechanical advantage} = \frac{\text{load}}{\text{effort}} = \frac{30}{15} = 2.$$

$$\text{Velocity ratio} = \frac{\text{distance moved by effort}}{\text{distance moved by load}} = \frac{1}{0.5} = 2.$$

$$\text{Efficiency} = \frac{\text{mechanical advantage}}{\text{velocity ratio}} \times 100\%$$

$$= \frac{2}{2} \times 100\%$$

$$= 100\%.$$

This is not a realistic example as no machine is 100% efficient. The losses due to friction and the weight of the pulleys and rope have not been taken into account.

Example 2
A pulley system is shown in Fig. 2.52. An effort of 22 N moves a load of 40 N. The effort moves 1 metre when the load is raised 0.5 metres. Assume the ropes and pulleys are weightless and the pulleys are frictionless. Calculate the efficiency of the system.

Fig. 2.52   A pulley system

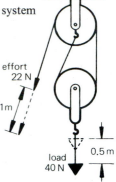

effort
22 N

1m

load
40 N

0.5 m

$$\text{Mechanical advantage} = \frac{\text{load}}{\text{effort}} = \frac{40}{22} = \frac{20}{11}.$$

$$\text{Velocity ratio} = \frac{\text{distance moved by effort}}{\text{distance moved by load}} = \frac{1 \text{ m}}{0.5 \text{ m}} = 2.$$

$$\text{Efficiency} = \frac{\text{mechanical advantage}}{\text{velocity ratio}} \times 100\%$$

$$= \frac{20}{11} \times \frac{1}{2} \times 100\%$$

$$= \frac{1000}{11}\%$$

$$= 90.9\%$$

Therefore, the machine is about 91 % efficient.

The efficiency of most engines is quite low. Most of the energy put into the engine as fuel is wasted in heat loss.

15   *Which one of these engines or machines is the most efficient? Which is the least efficient?*

Engine or Machine	Efficiency
Motor car engine	25%
Diesel engine	37%
Aircraft gas turbine	36%
Rocket motor	48%
Steam locomotive	8%
Large electric motor	90%
Nuclear power plant	30%

Answers to Questions

1   Rotary motion symbol.
2   Revs/min.
3   They are in the same direction.
4   The pulley changes the direction of the linear motion. As the effort moves down, the load rises (Fig. 2.2).

46

5   Home: car fan belt, washing machine, sewing machine, vacuum cleaner. School workshop: lathe, drilling machine, milling machine.

6   The driver pulley – engine crankshaft pulley. Driven pulleys – fan pulley and the generator pulley.

7   There is more surface area contact between the vee pulley and vee belt. Also, the vee belt has a wedging action (inclined plane) in the vee groove.

8   The belt is likely to slip.

9   Velocity ratio $= \dfrac{\text{distance moved by effort}}{\text{distance moved by load}}$

but effort distance = load distance
so velocity ratio = 1.

10   Use another single pulley as shown in Fig. 2.38.

11   10 newtons.

12   Mechanical advantage is 8, velocity ratio is 8.

13   In a garage, on a crane, moving loads in a factory, hoisting up a washing line of wet clothes.

14   Work done = force × distance moved by force.

15   Large electric motor (90% efficient). Steam locomotive (8% efficient).

3 Gears

■ **The Gear Wheel**

The **gear wheel** (Fig. 3.1) is a basic mechanism. Its purpose is to transmit rotary motion and force. A gear is a wheel with accurately machined teeth round its edge. A shaft passes through its centre and the gear may be keyed to the shaft. Gears are used in groups of two or more. A group of gears is called a **gear train** (Fig. 3.2).

Fig. 3.1   A gear wheel   Fig. 3.2   A gear train

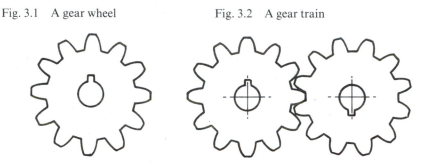

The gears in a train are arranged so that their teeth closely interlock or **mesh**. The teeth on meshing gears are the same size so that they are of equal strength. Also, the spacing of the teeth is the same on each gear.

The gears shown are called **spur gears** (probably because they resemble the spurs worn by horsemen). When two spur gears of different sizes mesh together, the larger gear is called a **wheel**, and the smaller gear is called a **pinion** (Fig. 3.3). In a simple gear train of two spur gears, the input motion and force are applied to the **driver gear**. The output motion and force are transmitted by the **driven gear**. The driver gear rotates the driven gear without slipping.

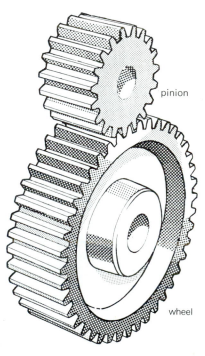

pinion

wheel

Fig. 3.3   Spur gears

The wheel or the pinion can be the driver gear. It depends on the exact function the designer wishes the mechanism to fulfil. When two spur gears are meshed (Fig. 3.4) the gears rotate in opposite directions.

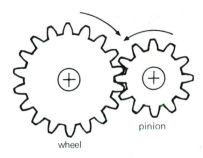

Fig. 3.4   The direction of rotation of meshed spur gears

■ Graphic Symbols

It is difficult, tedious and time consuming to draw all the teeth on a gear. A graphic symbol of two concentric circles is used to represent a gear (Fig. 3.5). The outer circle is the **tip circle** and represents a circle on which lie the tips of the gear teeth. The inner circle is the **root circle** and represents a circle on which lie the bottoms of the spaces between the teeth.

Fig. 3.5   a) A gear   b) Graphic symbol of a gear

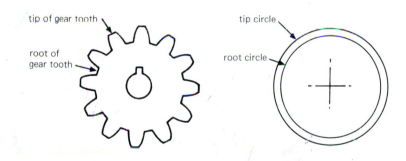

The two meshed gears shown in Fig. 3.6a can be represented by the graphic symbol shown in Fig. 3.6b.

Fig. 3.6   a) Meshed spur gears   b) Graphic symbol of meshed spur gears

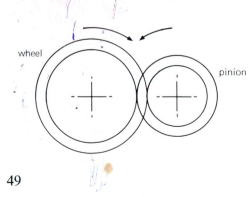

■ The Transmission of Rotary Motion

Figure 3.7 shows two meshed spur gears. Gear *B* is the driver gear and has 20 teeth. Gear *A* is thd driven gear and has 10 teeth. When driver gear *B* makes one complete revolution, all 20 of its teeth mesh with driven gear *A*. As driven gear *A* has only 10 teeth, it rotates twice to one revolution of driver gear *B*.

Fig. 3.7   a) Driver and driven gears

b) Graphic symbol of driver and driven gears

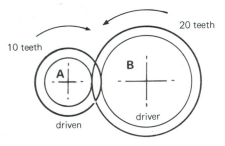

In this gear train, the driver gear supplies the effort while the driven gear is the load. The effort rotates one revolution for two revolutions of the load.

$$\text{Velocity ratio} = \frac{\text{distance moved by effort}}{\text{distance moved by load}}$$

$$= \frac{1 \text{ revolution}}{2 \text{ revolutions}}.$$

Therefore, velocity ratio is $\frac{1}{2}$.

Note that for this gear train of two gears,

$$\text{velocity ratio} = \frac{\text{number of teeth on driven gear } A \ (10)}{\text{number of teeth on driver gear } B \ (20)}$$

$$= \frac{1}{2}.$$

(Note that this does not apply to complex gear trains with many gear wheels.)

The velocity ratio of a gear train is often called the '**gear ratio**'. So, in the previous example, the velocity ratio is $\frac{1}{2}$ and the gear ratio is also $\frac{1}{2}$. It is more usual to write this as a ratio than as a fraction. So the gear ratio is $1:2$.

50

Example

Figure 3.8 shows two spur gears. The driver gear *B* has 20 teeth and the driven gear *A* has 40 teeth. What is the gear ratio of this mechanism?

Fig. 3.8   a) Driver and driven gears

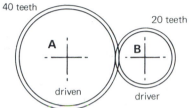

b) Graphic symbol of driver
and driven gears

One revolution of the driver gear *B* causes 20 teeth to mesh with 20 teeth of the driven gear *A*.

This is $\dfrac{20}{40} = \dfrac{1}{2}$ of the teeth of the driven gear *A*.

Thus the driven gear *A* has turned $\frac{1}{2}$ of a revolution.

Velocity ratio = gear ratio

$$= \frac{\text{input movement}}{\text{output movement}} = \frac{1}{\frac{1}{2}}$$

$$= 1 \times \frac{2}{1} = 2.$$

Therefore, gear ratio is 2:1.

■ Gear Shaft Velocities

In the gear mechanism shown in Fig. 3.9a, the shaft through the centre of the driver gear is called the **driver shaft**. The gears transmit motion and torque to the shaft attached to the driven gear. This shaft is called the **driven shaft**.

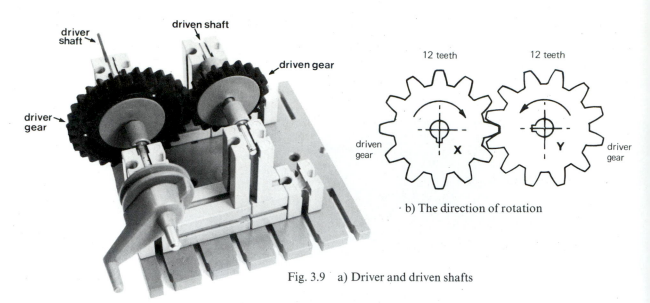

Fig. 3.9   a) Driver and driven shafts

b) The direction of rotation

The simple gear train shown in Fig. 3.9b has two meshed gears each with 12 teeth. One revolution of the driver gear *Y* causes 12 teeth to mesh with 12 teeth on the driven gear *X*.

1   What is the gear ratio of the meshed gears in Fig. 3.9b?

If the driver gear rotates at 600 revs/min, the driven gear rotates at 600 revs/min. But, the driven gear rotates in the opposite direction to the driver gear.

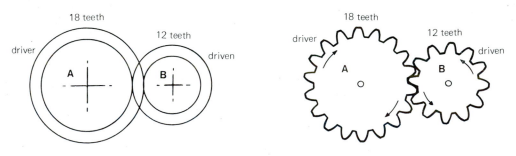

Fig. 3.10   a) Symbolic representation of meshed gears   b) Driver and driven gears

In Fig. 3.10 the driver gear *A* has 18 teeth and the driven gear *B* has 12 teeth. In one revolution of the driver gear *A*, its 18 teeth mesh with 18 teeth of the driven gear *B*. As the driven gear *B* has only 12 teeth, it must rotate 18/12 times for 18 teeth to mesh with the driver gear. So one revolution of the driver gear *A* produces 18/12, or 3/2, or $1\frac{1}{2}$ revolutions of the driven gear *B*. The gear ratio of this mechanism is 1:3/2. To express the ratio in the more usual form, both sides of the ratio are multiplied by 2 to give the ratio as 2:3. Therefore the gear ratio is 2:3.

If the driver gear rotates 200 revs/min, then the driven gear must rotate $200 \times \dfrac{18}{12}$ revs/min $= 200 \times \dfrac{3}{2} = 300$ revs/min.

From this example, it can be seen that

$$\frac{\text{velocity of driven gear}}{\text{velocity of driver gear}} = \frac{\text{number of teeth on driver gear}}{\text{number of teeth on driven gear}}$$

$$\frac{300}{200} = \frac{18}{12}$$

so velocity of driven gear

$$= \frac{\text{number of teeth on driver gear} \times \text{velocity of driver gear}}{\text{number of teeth on driven gear}}.$$

Therefore, velocity of driven gear $= \dfrac{18 \times 200}{12}$

$$= 300 \text{ revs/min.}$$

This is an increase in rotational velocity. It is accompanied by a decrease of torque.

Example
A driver gear *A* with 15 teeth is rotated at 400 revs/min. It meshes with a driven gear *B* with 60 teeth (Fig. 3.11). What is the velocity of the driven shaft?

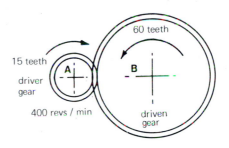

Fig. 3.11   An example of a gear train

Velocity of driven gear

$$= \frac{\text{number of teeth on driver gear} \times \text{velocity of driver gear}}{\text{number of teeth on driven gear}}$$

$$= \frac{15 \times 400}{60} = \frac{1 \times 400}{4}.$$

Therefore, velocity of driven gear and driven shaft is 100 revs/min.
This is a reduction in rotational velocity. It is accompanied by an increase in torque.

☐ **The Transmission of Force**

Gears are not only used to transmit motion, they are also used to transmit force. But, the force acts at a distance from a centre of rotation. Consider a spanner being used to tighten a nut (Fig. 3.12).

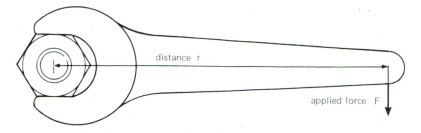

Fig. 3.12   Torque on a nut – force applied to a spanner

When a nut is tightened by a spanner, a force F is applied by hand at a distance r from the centre of the nut (the centre of rotation). The turning moment on the nut is the product of force $F \times$ distance r. The turning moment $F \times r$ is called a **torque**. Torque is measured in newton metres because the applied force is in newtons and the distance from the centre of rotation is measured in metres. If the same force F is applied to a longer spanner at distance R from the centre of rotation, the torque is greater. The nut is more firmly tightened, because the tightening effort or torque is greater. In this case, the effort is not a simple force but a torque, that is a force $\times$ a distance measured at right angles to the force.

When we consider two meshed gears, the spanner and nut relationship of Fig. 3.12 is reversed. Each gear tooth can be regarded as the end of a lever which has the centre of the gear as its centre of rotation. A motor or an engine applies a torque to the driver gear through its shaft. The result is a force F acting at the tip of a lever of length r. The torque produced, $F \times r$, is applied to the load, the driven gear.

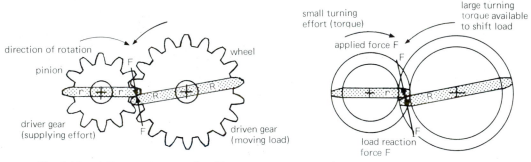

Fig. 3.13   a) Two gears are rather like two levers   b) Torque transmitted by gears

When two gear wheels the same size are meshed, they act as a simple torque transmitter. When two gears of differing size are meshed, they act as torque converters. In the example shown in Fig. 3.13a and b, a small torque has been converted into a large torque. This is because force F acts at radius r in the driver gear but at radius R in the driven gear. But, as you saw earlier there has been a decrease in rotational velocity. If the wheel was the driver and the pinion the driven gear, the situation would be reversed. A large torque would be converted into a small torque but there would be an increase in rotational velocity.

For a gear train,

$$\text{mechanical advantage} = \frac{\text{load torque}}{\text{effort torque}} = \frac{F \times R}{F \times r} = \frac{R}{r}.$$

Therefore, $\text{mechanical advantage} = \dfrac{\text{radius of driven gear}}{\text{radius of driver gear}}.$

As the number of teeth on each gear is proportional to the radius of the gear,

$$\text{mechanical advantage} = \frac{\text{number of teeth on driven gear}}{\text{number of teeth on driver gear}}.$$

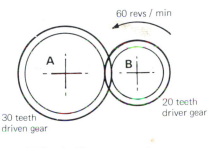

60 revs / min

30 teeth
driven gear

20 teeth
driver gear

b) Symbolic representation
of gear train example

Fig. 3.14   a) An example of a gear train

Example
Two meshed gears are shown in Fig. 3.14a and b. The driver gear *B* has 20 teeth and the driven gear *A* has 30 teeth. The driver gear *B* is rotated at 60 revs/min.
a) What is the mechanical advantage of the mechanism?
b) What is the gear ratio of the mechanism?
c) What is the rotary velocity of the driven gear?

$$\text{Mechanical advantage} = \frac{\text{number of teeth on driven gear}}{\text{number of teeth on driver gear}} = \frac{30}{20}$$

$$= \frac{3}{2} = 1\tfrac{1}{2}.$$

$$\text{Velocity ratio} = \text{gear ratio} = \frac{\text{input movement}}{\text{output movement}}$$

$$= \frac{1}{20/30} = 1 \times \frac{30}{20} = \frac{3}{2}.$$

Gear ratio is $\frac{3}{2}:1$, (multiplying by 2) $= 3:2$.

Velocity of driven gear

$$= \frac{\text{velocity of driver gear} \times \text{number of teeth on driver gear}}{\text{number of teeth on driven gear}}$$

$$= \frac{60 \times 20}{30} = 2 \times 20.$$

Therefore, velocity of driven gear is 40 revs/min.

Notice this gear mechanism has a mechanical advantage greater than 1, but at the cost of a velocity reduction.

■ Simple Gear Trains

A gear train can consist of just two meshed gears. The gear wheels rotate in opposite directions as shown in Fig. 3.15.

Fig. 3.15   The direction of rotation of two meshed gears

A **simple gear train** consists of two or more meshed gears, where the gear shafts are parallel, and there is only one meshed gear on each shaft. Fig. 3.16 shows a simple gear train of three meshed gears. The intermediate gear between the driver gear and the driven gear is called an **idler gear**.

Fig. 3.16   A simple gear train with an idler gear

The driver gear and the driven gear now rotate in the same direction. The idler gear does not alter the gear ratio between the driver and the driven gears. Nor does it alter the ratio of the rotary velocity of the driver shaft to the rotary velocity of the driven shaft. The idler gear only serves to keep the direction of rotation of the driven gear the same as the driver gear.

Example

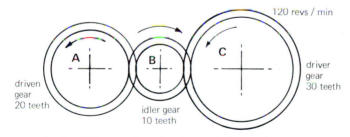

Fig. 3.17   An example of an idler gear in a simple gear train

In Fig. 3.17, the driver gear has 30 teeth, the idler gear has 10 teeth and the driven gear has 20 teeth.
a) What is the gear ratio of the gear train?
b) If the driver gear is rotated at 120 revs/min, what is the rotary velocity of the driven gear?

a) Velocity ratio or gear ratio between gear C and gear B

$$= \frac{\text{number of teeth on gear } B}{\text{number of teeth on gear } C} = \frac{10}{30}.$$

For gears C and B, gear ratio $= \frac{1}{3}$.

Gear ratios between gear B and gear A

$$= \frac{\text{number of teeth on gear } A}{\text{number of teeth on gear } B}$$

$$= \frac{20}{10}.$$

For gears B and A, gear ratio $= 2:1$.

Gear ratio between gear C and gear A is found by multiplying the intermediate gear ratios.

Therefore, gear ratio between gear C and gear $A = \dfrac{10}{30} \times \dfrac{20}{10} = \dfrac{20}{30}$

$$= \frac{2}{3} = 2:3.$$

The same result is obtained if the idler gear is ignored and A and C imagined as meshed together.

Gear ratio between gear C and gear A

$$= \frac{\text{number of teeth on driven gear}}{\text{number of teeth on driver gear}}$$

$$= \frac{20}{30}$$

$$= \frac{2}{3}.$$

Therefore, the gear ratio of the simple gear train is $2:3$.

b) To calculate the rotational velocity of the driven gear, ignore the effect of the idler gear.

Velocity of driven gear

$$= \frac{\text{velocity of driver gear} \times \text{number of teeth on driver gear}}{\text{number of teeth on driven gear}}$$

$$= \frac{120 \times 30}{20} = 180 \text{ revs/min}.$$

Notice the driver gear and the driven gear rotate in the same direction.

☐ Compound Gear Trains

The **compound gear train** shown in Fig. 3.18 consists of two pairs of meshed gears where the gear shafts are parallel. The gear train has a driver gear and a driven gear, but the intermediate gears are fixed together on one common shaft. The gear wheels on the intermediate shaft are not idlers, for one is a driven gear and the other is a driver gear. They do affect the output of the gear train.

Fig. 3.18   A compound gear train

Example

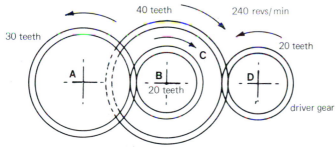

Fig. 3.19   An example of a compound gear train

A compound gear train shown in Fig. 3.19 has two pairs of meshed gears: A and B, and C and D. Gear A has 30 teeth, gear B has 20 teeth, gear C has 40 teeth and gear D has 20 teeth. The driver gear D rotates at 240 revs/min.
a) What is the gear ratio of the compound gear train?
b) What is the rotary velocity of gear A?

59

a) Gear ratio or velocity ratio $= \dfrac{\text{number of teeth on driven gear}}{\text{number of teeth on driver gear}}$.

For gears C and D,

gear ratio $= \dfrac{\text{number of teeth on gear } C}{\text{number of teeth on gear } D}$

$= \dfrac{40}{20} = \dfrac{2}{1}$

Therefore, the gear ratio of gears C and D is $2:1$.

For gears A and B,

gear ratio $= \dfrac{\text{number of teeth on gear } A}{\text{number of teeth on gear } B}$

$= \dfrac{30}{20} = \dfrac{3}{2}$.

Therefore, the gear ratio of gears A and B is $3:2$.

The gear ratio of the compound train can be found by multiplying the individual gear ratios.

Gear ratio of compound gear train $= \dfrac{2}{1} \times \dfrac{3}{2}$

$= \dfrac{3}{1}$.

Therefore, the compound gear train has a gear ratio of $3:1$.

b) If the gear ratio of the compound gear train is $3:1$, there is a velocity reduction of $3:1$, i.e. the velocity of the driven gear A is $\frac{1}{3}$ of the rotary velocity of the driver gear D. The velocity of the driver gear D is 240 revs/min.

Therefore, velocity of driven gear $A = \dfrac{1}{3} \times 240$

$= 80$ revs/min.

    2   *Figure 3.20 shows a crane winding mechanism. What type of gear train is used for the winding mechanism?*

    3   *The driver gear in Fig. 3.20 is rotated by a motor or engine. Does the gear mechanism increase or decrease the rotary velocity of the winding drum?*

One of the most common applications of simple and compound gear trains is to drive the lead screw on a metalwork lathe. Lathe operations such as screw cutting require the cutting tool to move along the rotating piece of work at a steady rate. The cutting tool is mounted in a toolpost on the cross slide and saddle of the lathe. The saddle and toolpost are driven by a rotating lead screw.

Fig. 3.20   A crane winding mechanism

Simple and compound gear trains are built up from a collection of gear wheels in order to drive the lead screw from the rotating spindle shaft of the lathe (Fig. 3.21).

Fig. 3.21   The movement of the lathe tool in relation to the rotation of the work

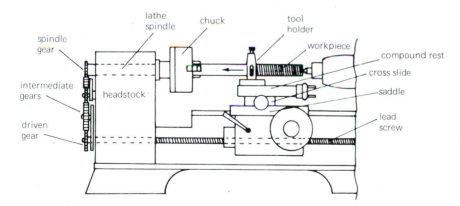

The gear attached to the end of the lathe spindle can be meshed to a tumbler reversing mechanism (Fig. 3.22). Two idler gears are used to enable the spindle to rotate the first driver gear of the gear train in a forward (Fig. 3.22a) or

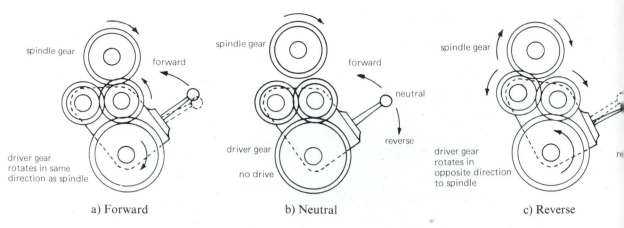

spindle gear

forward

driver gear
rotates in same
direction as spindle

a) Forward

spindle gear

forward

neutral

reverse

driver gear

no drive

b) Neutral

spindle gear

driver gear
rotates in
opposite direction
to spindle

c) Reverse

Fig. 3.22   A tumbler reverse gear mechanism

reverse (Fig. 3.22c) direction. The tumbler gear mechanism can also be put into a neutral position when no drive is required to the driver gear from the spindle gear (Fig. 3.22b).

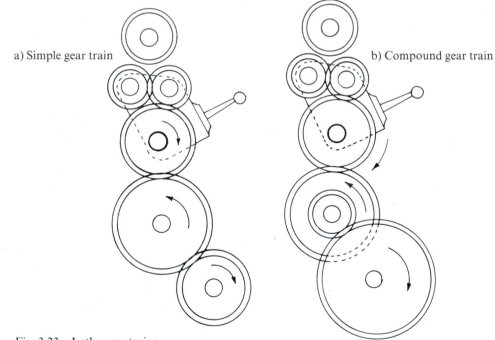

a) Simple gear train

b) Compound gear train

Fig. 3.23   Lathe gear trains

The transmission of motion and torque to the lead screw from the driver gear of the tumbler mechanism is achieved by the use of simple (Fig. 3.23a) or compound (Fig. 3.23b) gear trains. Gear wheels are selected from a matching range of gear sizes. This allows alteration of the gear ratio between the driver and the lead screw.

■ Designing a Simple Gearbox

Assume that you have an electric motor which rotates at 240 revs/min, and that you want it to turn a window display unit at 10 revs/min. The direction of the rotation is not important. Design a gearbox that will reduce the velocity of the motor from 240 revs/min to 10 revs/min.

Fig. 3.24   A block diagram of the display system

The complete display system can be drawn as a block diagram (Fig. 3.24). The problem can be expressed in 'black box' form (Fig. 3.25). The gearbox must produce a velocity reduction of 240:10, i.e. a velocity reduction of 24:1. The input and output shafts are assumed to be parallel.

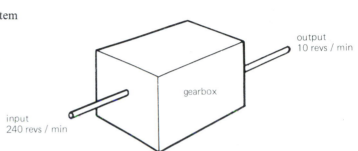

Fig. 3.25   'Black box' representation of the gearbox problem

There are many solutions to this design problem. The velocity reduction can be achieved by a small driver pinion rotating a large driven gear wheel. However, the reduction required cannot be achieved with the gears available in your construction kit. The velocity reduction can be obtained by using three pairs of meshed spur gears. For example, a velocity reduction of 4:1, and then 3:1 and finally 2:1 can be used. These figures are obtained by breaking down the overall ratio (24:1) into prime factors.

A diagram of this solution is shown in Fig. 3.26. The first pair of gears has a gear ratio of 4:1, the second pair has a gear ratio of 3:1 and the third pair has a gear ratio of 2:1. Each pair of gears causes a velocity reduction.

Fig. 3.26   Diagram of a gearbox solution

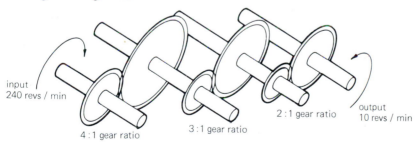

The selection of appropriate gears for the gearbox depends on those available in the construction kit. The gear ratios required to solve this problem can be achieved by combining gears with different numbers of teeth.

63

MECCANO

The Meccano kit has the following spur gears:

pinions – 25 teeth, 19 teeth and 15 teeth;

gear wheels – 50 teeth, 57 teeth and 60 teeth.

The required gear ratios can be obtained by using

60 teeth and 15 teeth – 4:1

57 teeth and 19 teeth – 3:1

50 teeth and 25 teeth – 2:1.

One possible solution is shown in Fig. 3.27 with the Meccano gears that can be used to make the gearbox.

Fig. 3.27   a) A simple gearbox solution   b) Meccano gears

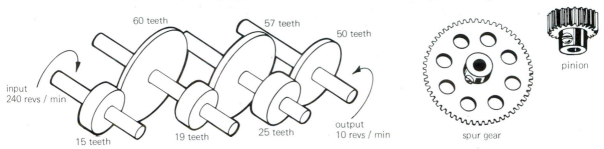

FISCHERTECHNIK

The Fischertechnik kit contains the following range of nylon gears:

10 teeth, 20 teeth, 30 teeth and 40 teeth.

The required gear ratios can be obtained using

40 teeth and 10 teeth – 4:1

30 teeth and 10 teeth – 3:1

40 teeth and 20 teeth – 2:1

or 20 teeth and 10 teeth – 2:1.

One possible solution is shown in Fig. 3.28. Figure 3.29 shows the Fischertechnik gears that can be used to make the gearbox.

Fig. 3.28   A simple gearbox solution

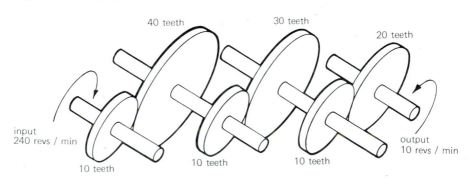

a)

Fig. 3.29   Fischertechnik gears

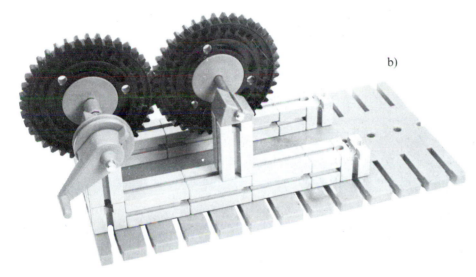

b)

Answers to Questions
1   Gear ratio is 1:1.
2   Compound gear train.
3   It decreases the rotary velocity of the motor to give a slower rotary velocity to the winding drum.

4 Gear Mechanisms

■ **Gear Materials**

1 Give examples of the use of gears in the following situations:
   a) the home;
   b) the motor car;
   c) the workshop;
   d) industry.

Gears are made from a number of materials, e.g. steel, plastic, brass pinion wire, brass and cast iron. The machines we use at home or at work contain many different kinds of gears made in various ways from different materials. Gears are also used in toys, models and clockwork motors but they are not accurately machined (Fig. 4.1). They are produced cheaply by stamping them from thin sheet mild steel. Pinion gears are made from extruded brass pinion wire.

Fig. 4.1   a) Sheet metal gears used in models

b) A gear train driven by an electric motor – note the use of a plastic gear

Plastic gears are quiet and smooth-running. Sometimes a plastic gear is included in a train of metal gears to reduce noise. Such a gear is called a silent gear (Fig. 4.1b).

Fig. 4.2   Fischertechnik nylon gears

Plastic gears are usually made from tough plastics, like nylon. They can be machined or made by injection moulding, e.g. Fischertechnik gears (Fig. 4.2) and industrial gears and pulleys (Fig. 4.3).

Fig. 4.3   Plastic gears and toothed pulleys

2 Give an application of plastic gears where it is essential to have a silent, smooth gear mechanism.

Many of the gears in the Meccano kit are made from brass. They have a central boss which has a grub or set screw to key the gear to its shaft.

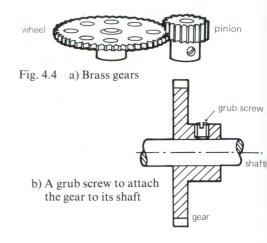

Fig. 4.4 a) Brass gears

Brass gears are often used in clocks where they work well without any lubricant. Oil causes dust to adhere to the gears and this causes gear-tooth wear. An advantage of brass gears is that constant meshing work hardens their teeth. Because of this, the brass gears in well used old clocks often show little sign of wear.

b) A grub screw to attach the gear to its shaft

The majority of the gears made by industry for engineering machinery are made of steel because of its strength (Fig. 4.5). Many steel gears are heat-treated to improve their wear-resistant properties. For example, the teeth of mild steel gears are often case-hardened to make them more wear resistant. In this process the tough mild steel is given a very thin outer casing of hard carbon steel by dipping it in a chemical rich in carbon and then heat-treating.

Fig. 4.5 A wide range of machined steel gears

Large gear wheels are usually made of cast iron.

3 *Can you find any examples of cast iron gear wheels in the school workshop?*

Steel and cast iron gears are usually attached to their shafts by a key (Fig. 4.6). A keyway is cut in the gear and the driving shaft. A tapered steel key is driven into the keyway to secure the gear. Keys and keyways can take many different forms.

Fig. 4.6   Use of a key to secure a gear

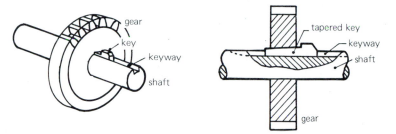

■ Gearbox Design – Transmission through a Right Angle

An engineer has to design a gearbox with an output shaft at right angles to the input shaft. The problem can be expressed in 'black box' form (Fig. 4.7). The following are some gear mechanisms which can be considered as solutions to the problem.

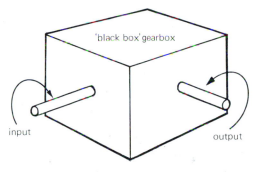

Fig. 4.7   'Black box' gearbox – transmission of motion through a right angle

Bevel gears have teeth cut on a cone instead of a cylinder blank. They are used in pairs to transmit rotary motion and torque where the bevel gear shafts are at right angles (90 degrees) to each other (Fig. 4.8).

Fig. 4.8   Bevel gears

Fig. 4.9   A hand drill or wheel brace – use of bevel gears

Bevel gears are used in a wheel brace or hand drill (Fig. 4.9). The bevel gear mechanism used in the hand drill produces an increase in rotary velocity. The large bevel gear wheel is turned by hand. The chuck attached to the small bevel gear rotates at a much faster velocity than the hand wheel.

Bevel gears can be represented by a graphic symbol (Fig. 4.10a). Meshed gears are represented by the graphic symbol shown in Fig. 4.10b.

Fig. 4.10   Graphic symbols

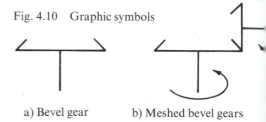

a) Bevel gear   b) Meshed bevel gears

When the meshed bevel gears are the same size and have an equal number of teeth, they are called **mitre gears**. No rotary velocity increase or reduction occurs when mitre gears are used, but rotary motion and torque are transmitted through a right angle (Fig. 4.11).

Fig. 4.11   a) Mitre gears   b) Graphic symbol of mitre gears

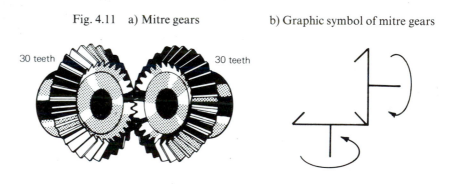

30 teeth   30 teeth

4   Give an example of the use of a bevel gear in kitchen equipment.

Crossed helical gears also transmit rotary motion and torque through a right angle. The teeth of a helical gear are inclined at an angle to the axis of rotation of the gear. Figure 4.12 shows how the axes of rotation of two helical gears are crossed at right angles. Helical gears are smoother running than spur gears and are more suitable for rotation at high velocities.

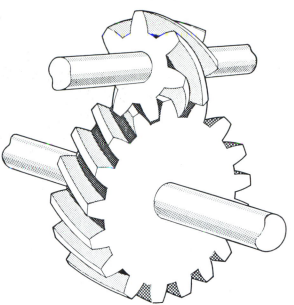

Fig. 4.12   Crossed helical gears

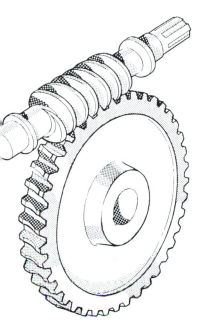

Fig. 4.13   A worm and wormwheel

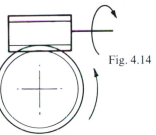

Fig. 4.14   Graphic symbol of a worm and wormwheel

A gear which has one tooth is called a **worm**. The tooth is in the form of a screw thread. A **wormwheel** meshes with the worm (Fig. 4.13.). The wormwheel is a helical gear with teeth inclined so that they can engage with the thread-like worm. Like mitre and crossed helical gears, the worm and wormwheel transmit torque and rotary motion through a right angle. The worm always drives the wormwheel and never the other way round. The mechanism locks if the wormwheel tries to drive the worm. Worm mechanisms are very quiet running.

The graphic symbol for a worm and wormwheel is shown in Fig. 4.14. A considerable velocity reduction can be achieved by using a worm and wormwheel. The gear ratio of a meshed worm and wormwheel is

$$\frac{\text{number of teeth on wormwheel}}{\text{number of teeth on worm}}.$$

As the worm acts like a single toothed gear, so the gear ratio of worm and

$$\text{wormwheel} = \frac{\text{number of teeth on wormwheel}}{1}.$$

Example

The wormwheel in Fig. 4.13 has 40 teeth and the worm has one tooth.

Gear ratio of worm and wormwheel $= \dfrac{40}{1}$.

Gear ratio = 40 : 1.

This gives a rotary velocity reduction of 40 : 1.

☐ Special Gears and Applications

Several other types of gears are used in engineering. The helical gear is used for applications that require very quiet and smooth running at high rotational velocities. **Parallel helical gears** have their teeth inclined at a small angle to their axis of rotation. Each tooth is part of a spiral or helix. The helical gears shown in Fig. 4.15a have splines cut in their centre holes. The gears can move along a splined (grooved) shaft, although they rotate with the shaft. Helical gears are used in motorcar gearboxes (Fig. 4.16). **Double helical gears** give an efficient transfer of torque and smooth motion at very high rotational velocities (Fig. 4.15b).

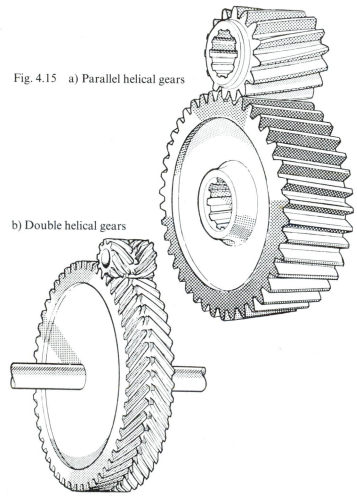

Fig. 4.15   a) Parallel helical gears

b) Double helical gears

Fig. 4.16
a) Helical gears – main shaft of a motorcar gearbox
b) Helical gears in a motorcar gearbox

When it is necessary to transmit quietly and smoothly a large torque through a right angle at high velocities, **spiral bevel gears** can be used (Fig. 4.17). Spiral bevel gears have teeth cut in a helix spiral form on the surface of a cone. They are quieter running than straight bevel gears and have a longer life. Spiral bevel gears are used in motorcar rear axle gearboxes.

Fig. 4.17   Spiral bevel gears

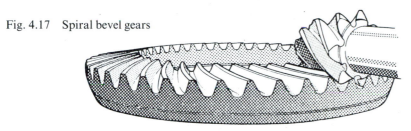

It is possible to cut gear teeth on the face of a gear wheel (Fig. 4.18a). Also, gear teeth can be cut on the inside of a gear ring (Fig. 4.18b). Internal gears have better load-carrying capacity than external spur gears. They are safer in use because the teeth are guarded.

Fig. 4.18   a) Face cut gears

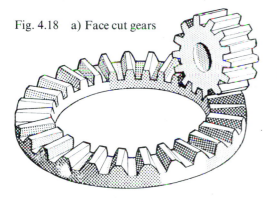

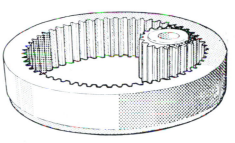

b) Internal gears

■ Converting Rotary Motion to Linear Motion

A **rack and pinion** mechanism is used to transform rotary motion into linear motion and vice versa. A round spur gear, the pinion, meshes with a spur gear which has teeth set in a straight line, the rack (Fig. 4.19). The rack and pinion can transform rotary motion into linear motion and vice versa in three ways:

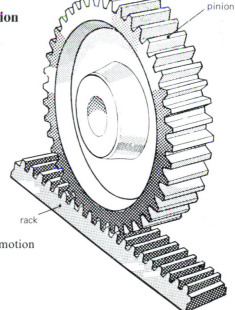

pinion

rack

Fig. 4.19   Rack and pinion motion

73

a) rotation of the pinion about a fixed centre causes the rack to move in a straight line;
b) movement of the rack in a straight line causes the pinion to rotate about a fixed centre;
c) if the rack is fixed and the pinion rotates, then the pinion's centre moves in a straight line taking the pinion with it.

The rack and pinion mechanism can be represented by a graphic symbol (Fig. 4.20).

When a pinion is turned, the linear movement of the rack is determined by the number of teeth per metre on the rack and the number of teeth on the pinion.

Fig. 4.20   Graphic symbol of a rack and pinion

Fig. 4.21   Rack and pinion calculation

Example

A rack with 200 teeth per metre is meshed with a pinion which has 20 teeth (Fig. 4.21). If the pinion is rotated through one revolution, how far does the rack move?

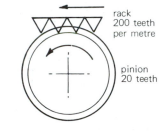

The pinion rotates one revolution, which is equivalent to 20 teeth. If the pinion is meshed with the rack, then the rack moves 20 teeth.

There are 200 teeth per metre on the rack, so the distance moved by the rack is

$$\frac{20 \text{ teeth}}{200 \text{ teeth}} \times 1 \text{ metre} = \tfrac{1}{10} \text{ metre} = 100 \text{ mm.}$$

Therefore, the rack moves 100 mm for every revolution of the pinion. Figures 4.22 and 4.23 show several applications of the rack and pinion.

Fig. 4.22   Rack and pinion mechanisms
        a) Linear movement of carriage on a lathe   b) Drilling machine feed mechanism

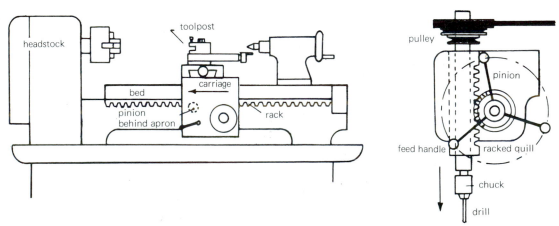

Fig. 4.23   a) Rack and pinion used to operate
sluice gates in watercress beds

b) Worm and wormwheel operate a
rack and pinion

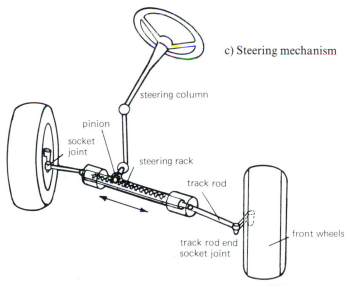

c) Steering mechanism

steering column

pinion

socket
joint

steering rack

track rod

track rod end
socket joint

front wheels

■ Construction Kits and Motors

The Meccano construction kit contains its own special kind of gear for transmitting motion and torque through a right angle. It is called a **contrate gear** (Fig. 4.24). It has teeth on the gear face and is used with pinion gears. The construction kit has two contrate gear wheels, one with 50 teeth and the other with 25 teeth.

The construction kit also has bevel gears and a pair of helical gears (Fig. 4.25).

Fig. 4.24   A contrate gear wheel

Fig. 4.25   a) Bevel gears

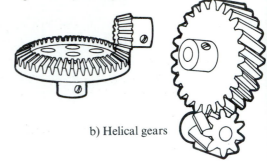

b) Helical gears

The Meccano worm is like a helical screw thread (Fig. 4.26). Since the worm acts like a gear with only one tooth, it produces a considerable velocity reduction when meshed with a pinion. The worm mechanism shown in Fig. 4.27 also transmits motion through a right angle. This mechanism could be used to drive the rear axle of a small vehicle.

Fig. 4.27   A worm and pinion used to drive the rear axle of a vehicle

Fig. 4.26   The Meccano worm

Small vehicles and mechanisms can be powered by the Meccano electric motor (Fig. 4.28). It works from a 3–12 volt dc supply. As the motor rotates at up to 2300 revs/min on a 6-volt supply some velocity reduction is necessary. The motor is fitted with a gearbox which gives the following six output ratios:

3:1   low torque – high rotary velocity

6:1

12:1

16:1

32:1

60:1   high torque – low rotary velocity.

Fig. 4.28   The Meccano electric motor and gearbox

The Meccano kit contains a rack strip which can be used with a pinion for rack and pinion applications (Fig. 4.29).

Fig. 4.29   The Meccano
             rack strip

FISCHERTECHNIK

The Fischertechnik kit contains large spur gears with 40 teeth around the rim. These can be meshed with other spur gear wheels and pinions to form gear trains (Fig. 4.30). The large spur gears also have teeth on the face. They can be used with a pinion to transmit motion through a right angle (Fig. 4.31). On the face ring there are 32 teeth.

Fig. 4.30   Fischertechnik spur gear trains   Fig. 4.31   Transmission through a right angle –
                                                                   use of face teeth

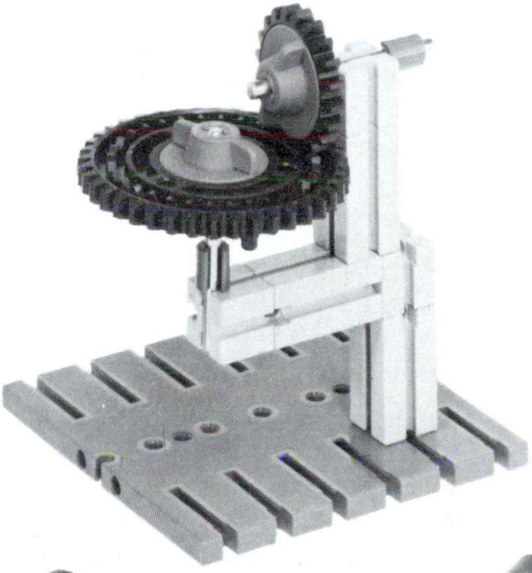

The Fischertechnik bevel gears
(Fig. 4.32) are really mitre gears.
These gears are used in pairs for
transmission through a right angle.
Each gear has 12 teeth.

Fig. 4.32   Fischertechnik bevel gears (mitre gears)

Fig. 4.33   a) The Fischertechnik rack
                 b) Using the rack with spur gears

The Fischertechnik rack can be attached to the building blocks. It can be used with spur gears meshed on either edge or on the face of the rack (Fig. 4.33a and b).

The kit contains a worm gear which can be used for velocity reduction and transmission through a right angle (Fig. 4.34). A worm gear is also attached to the spindle of the electric motor.

The Fischertechnik 6-volt motor (Fig. 4.35) operates from a dc power supply of up to 6.8 volts (a $4\frac{1}{2}$- volt battery can be used).

Fig. 4.34   The Fischertechnik worm and wormwheel

Fig. 4.35   The Fischertechnik electric motor

b) Worm drive to spur gear

c) Alternative drive
to spur gear

Fig. 4.36   a) Mounting the motor on a base plate

The motor can be mounted on a base
plate (Fig. 4.36a). It can be used to
drive spur gears and mechanisms as
shown in Fig. 4.36b and c.

Further velocity reductions can be achieved
by the addition to the motor of an extra
worm stand or a gear stand (Fig. 4.37).

The motor can be mounted on a small vehicle chassis
and used to drive the back axle as shown in Fig. 4.38.

4.37   Attachment of worm stand
and gear stand to the motor

Fig. 4.38   The Fischertechnik motor used to
drive a small vehicle

79

☐ Design Problem: A Small Vehicle

Design a small vehicle that will move 10 metres in one minute. It must be constructed from Fischertechnik components.

The problem can be expressed in block diagram form (Fig. 4.39). Suppose the Fischertechnik motor rotates at 1400 revs/min. The motor has a worm gear attached to its spindle. Worm and wormwheel is therefore the obvious method of velocity reduction. This also transmits the drive through a right angle. The size of the road wheels is 45 mm diameter.

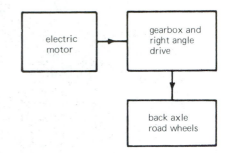

Fig. 4.39   Block diagram of small vehicle design problem

Circumference of a road wheel is $\pi \times$ diameter
$$= \pi \times 45 \text{ mm}$$
$$= 3.14 \times 0.045 \text{ metres}$$
$$= 0.1413 \text{ metres.}$$

Number of rotations of the road wheels in 10 metres
$$= \frac{\text{distance moved by vehicle}}{\text{circumference of road wheel}} = \frac{10 \text{ metres}}{0.1413 \text{ metres}}$$
$$= 70.7 \text{ rotations.}$$

The road wheels have to rotate about 70 revolutions in one minute if the vehicle is to move 10 metres in one minute. If the electric motor rotates at 1400 revs/min, the velocity reduction required is
$$\frac{1400}{70} = \frac{20}{1} \quad \text{i.e. } 20:1.$$

If the motor is mounted longitudinally on the vehicle then, in order to turn the back axle, a right angle drive is required.

A right angle drive with speed reduction of 20:1 can be achieved with a worm and a wormwheel with 20 teeth (Fig. 4.40). The completed model is shown in Fig. 4.38. An alternative solution is to use a worm and a wormwheel with 10 teeth. The wormwheel then meshes with a gear wheel with 20 teeth (Fig. 4.41).

Fig. 4.40   A possible solution to the small vehicle design problem

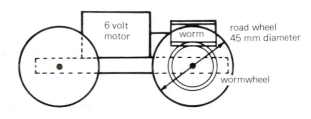

Fig. 4.41   An alternative solution to the small vehicle design problem

5   *What is the difference in the direction of motion of the two vehicles shown in Figs. 4.38 and 4.41?*

■ Gear Production

Metal gears for precision work are manufactured by machining. The gears are cut by removing metal from a blank. The basic machining methods are:
a) **milling** with a shaped cutter;
b) **shaping** or planing with a form tool or cutter;
c) **hobbing** – cutting with a hob.

To produce spur gears on a milling machine, a rotating gear cutter is used. The cutter's profile (the shape needing to be milled) is that of the space between the gear teeth to be cut (Fig. 4.42).

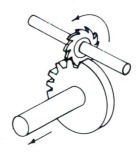

Fig. 4.42   Milling a gear with a form cutter

After each cut the gear blank is rotated slightly by a precise amount. This gives correct tooth number, size and spacing round the blank. This step-by-step rotation is called 'indexing'. It is performed by an indexing device called a 'dividing head'. This is attached to the milling machine table.

Gears can be shaped by moving a formed cutter past the gear blank. A rack-shaped cutter (Fig. 4.43) is moved to and fro parallel to the axis of the gear blank. The gear blank is slowly rotated in synchrony with the rack cutter movement.

Fig. 4.43   Rack cutter gear shaping

The production of bevel gears is a precise and complex process. The teeth diminish in size and vary in the curvature of their sides from the outer end of the tooth to the inner. A planing machine (Fig. 4.44) is used. Two planing tools are used, one for each side of the tooth. They rotate and reciprocate in synchrony with the gear blank.

Fig. 4.44   Planing a large bevel gear

Fig. 4.45   Generating a large spiral bevel gear

Large quantities of gears are produced by a machining process called 'hobbing'. A hob is a screw-shaped cutter, rather like a worm. Axial cuts are made through its helix to create a large number of cutting edges. The hob is rotated at a high speed velocity and is fed slowly across the rotating gear blank (Fig. 4.46).

Fig. 4.46   Hobbing a helical gear

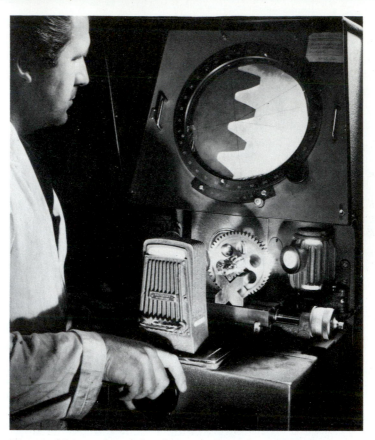

Fig. 4.47   Measuring angles of gear profiles at inspection stage

Large precision gears are often finished by grinding. Many gears made of steel are hardened by heat treatment. Often the surfaces of gear teeth are given a hardening treatment (case hardening) to improve their wear properties. The individual gear sizes and angles are checked and measured at the final inspection stage often with the aid of special optical equipment (Fig. 4.47).

Answers to Questions

1 a) In the kitchen – egg whisk, food mixers;
       in the home – clocks, watches, toys, clockwork motors.
    b) Gearboxes, differential gearboxes.
    c) Speed reduction gearboxes on power tools such as electric drills, lathes.
    d) Gearboxes in machine tools, winding mechanisms.
2 A fixed spool fishing reel or the focusing drive mechanism on an automatic slide projector.
3 The large gear wheel in a shaping machine (bull gear); large gears on the lathe.
4 Egg whisk.
5 The vehicles go in opposite directions (providing the motors revolve in the same direction). The motor would have to be reversed on one vehicle to make them both go in the same direction.

5 Cams, Eccentrics and Ratchets

■ Cams

A cam is a specially shaped piece of metal or plastic. The edge, or profile, of the cam guides the motion of a follower. A cam may be given an input motion that is rotary or reciprocating. A cam converts this input motion into a reciprocating output motion of the follower (Fig. 5.1). The cam normally rotates with constant velocity of rotation.

Fig. 5.1   a) A cam and follower – rotary motion to reciprocating motion

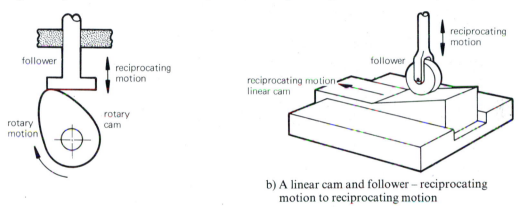

b) A linear cam and follower – reciprocating motion to reciprocating motion

The design of the cam shape controls the motion of the follower. Complex **cam profiles** or shapes can be made that will guide machine tool cutters along curved paths to reproduce complex shapes with great accuracy.

1   Give an example of where cams are used to open valves.

■ Cam Motion

In Fig. 5.2, a pear-shaped cam is used in a valve control mechanism. The valve is acting as the follower in this mechanism. When the valve is full open (Fig. 5.2a) the follower is in contact with the highest point of the cam, its crown. When the valve is closed, the follower is in contact with the lowest part of the cam, its heel (Fig. 5.2b). One complete rotation of the cam, where the valve opens and closes, is called a **cycle**. The valve is stationary in a closed position for just over half a cycle (Fig. 5.2b). When the follower is stationary it is said to **dwell**. The dwell portion of the cam is shown in Fig. 5.2d and its shape is a curve of constant radius.

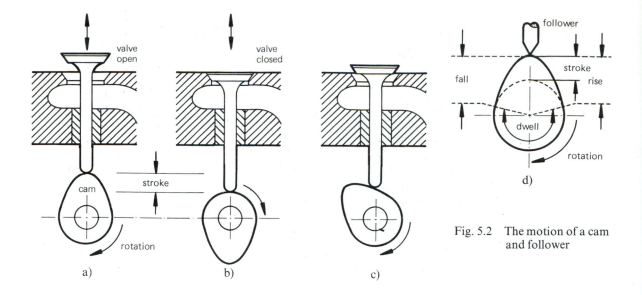

Fig. 5.2   The motion of a cam and follower

When not on the dwell part of the cam cycle, the follower rises and falls and the valve opens and closes. The section of the cam that causes the valve or follower to lift is called the **rise**. The section of the cam that allows the valve or follower to close is called the **fall**. The distance between the highest and lowest points on the cam profile is called the **stroke** of the cam. The distance the valve opens is the same as the stroke of the cam.

> 2   *Consider the cam mechanism shown in Fig. 5.2c. The direction of rotation of the cam is clockwise. Is the valve opening or closing?*

■ Types of Cam and Follower

A follower can slide or roll on the edge or surface of a cam. Fig. 5.3 shows some different types of follower.

Fig. 5.3   Different types of follower

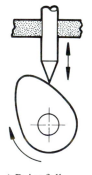

a) Point follower

b) Sliding and oscillating follower

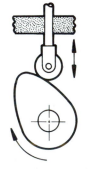

c) Roller follower

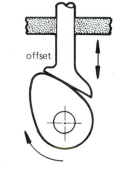

d) Angled foot follower

86

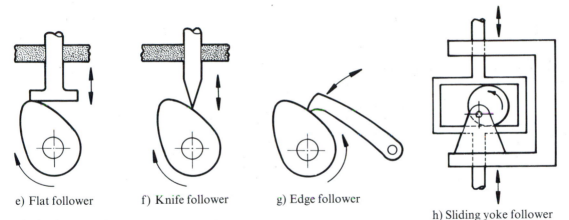

e) Flat follower   f) Knife follower   g) Edge follower

h) Sliding yoke follower

Fig. 5.3 (*continued*)

A follower can be kept in contact with a cam by its own weight, or by the forces acting through a lever or linkage, or by a spring (Fig. 5.4).

Fig. 5.4   Springs used to keep the follower in contact with the cam

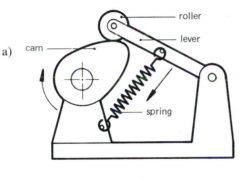

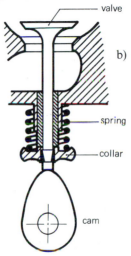

In Fig. 5.4b the spring also serves to keep the valve firmly closed when the cam is in its lowest position.

    A roller trip pneumatic valve can be cam-operated (Fig. 5.5). An edge follower is used in the distributor of a motorcar to open the contact points (Fig. 5.6). Notice that the contact points are closed by a spring.

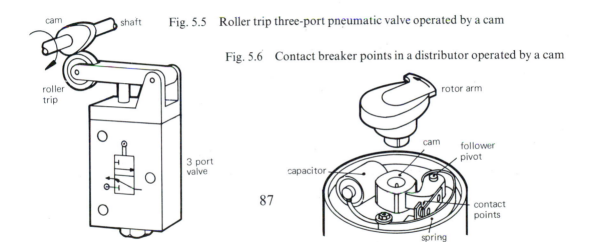

Fig. 5.5   Roller trip three-port pneumatic valve operated by a cam

Fig. 5.6   Contact breaker points in a distributor operated by a cam

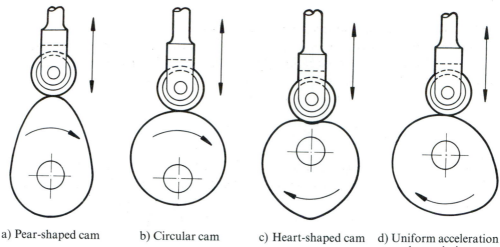

a) Pear-shaped cam   b) Circular cam   c) Heart-shaped cam   d) Uniform acceleration and retardation cam

Fig. 5.7   Profile shapes of some cams

The most common kind of cam is the **plate cam**. It consists of a narrow plate or disc which is fixed to a rotating shaft. The plate is shaped so that the follower will produce a pre-determined form of motion (Fig. 5.7). Most cams are designed to have a smooth curved shape so that the motion transmitted to the follower is smooth and without sudden jerks.

PEAR-SHAPED CAMS

Pear-shaped cams are often used for controlling valves. For example, they are used on motorcar cam shafts to operate the engine's valves. A follower controlled by a pear-shaped cam remains motionless for about half a revolution of the cam. During the time that the follower is stationary, the cam is in a dwell period. During the other half revolution of the cam, the follower rises and then falls. As the pear-shape cam is symmetrical, the rise motion is the same as the fall motion (Fig. 5.7a).

CIRCULAR CAMS

Circular cams are sometimes called eccentric cams. The cam profile is a circle. The centre of rotation of the cam is offset from the geometric centre of the circle. The circular cam produces a smooth form of motion called **simple harmonic motion**. These cams are often used to produce motion in pumps. Circular cams are also used to operate steam engine valves. As the cam is symmetrical, the rise and fall motions are the same (Fig. 5.7b).

HEART-SHAPED CAMS

The **heart-shaped cam** causes the follower to move with a **uniform velocity**. Heart-shaped cams are essential when the follower motion needs to be uniform or steady as, for example, in the mechanism that winds thread evenly on the bobbin of a sewing machine. A heart-shaped cam can be used for winding wire evenly on the former of a solenoid (Fig. 5.7c).

UNIFORM ACCELERATION AND RETARDATION CAMS

A cam shaped as shown in Fig. 5.7d controls the motion of the follower so that it moves with uniform acceleration and retardation. The follower gains and loses velocity at a constant rate. Uniform acceleration and retardation cams are used to control the motion of linkages and levers in complex machinery.

☐ Examples of Cams

If the edge of a flat plate is shaped, the profile can be used to guide the motion of a follower. Figure 5.8 shows a **flat plate cam** which moves with reciprocating motion. The roller follower also moves with reciprocating motion. These cams are often used on automatic machine tools. For example, the cutting tools on automatic lathes are sometimes guided by flat plate cams to produce many identical pieces of complex turned work.

Fig. 5.8   A flat plate cam – side of plate

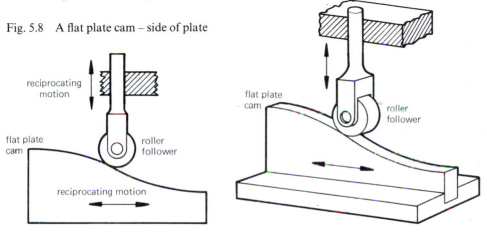

A flat plate cam can consist of a curved groove milled in a plate. The profile of the groove guides the follower (Fig. 5.9).

A groove can be milled in the face of cam discs. As the cam rotates, a follower located in the groove has its motion guided by the groove. This type of cam is called a **box cam** (Fig. 5.10).

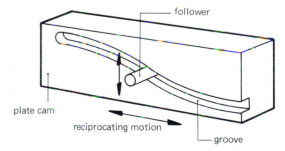

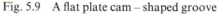

Fig. 5.9   A flat plate cam – shaped groove

Fig. 5.10   A box cam

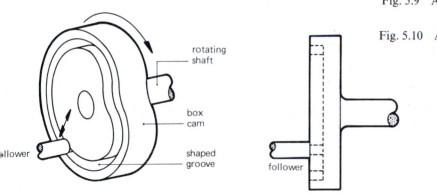

A nylon box cam can be found in the winding mechanism of a fixed spool fishing reel. It is used to spread the fishing line evenly over the spool when reeling in.

Swash plate cams are often used in pump mechanisms. **A swash plate cam** is a disc which is fixed to a rotating shaft. The disc is attached at an angle to the axis of rotation of the shaft (Fig. 5.11).

Fig. 5.11   A swash plate cam

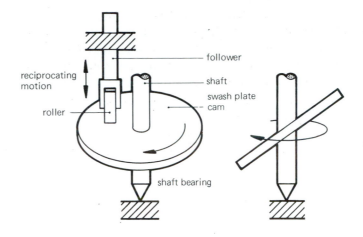

Cylindrical cams are used when motion has to be transmitted parallel to the axis of rotation of the cam. The cylindrical or **barrel cam** consists of a rotating cylinder with a helical (screw shaped) groove in its curved surface (Fig. 5.12). A follower with a tapered roller end is located in the groove. As the cylinder turns, the follower moves in a straight line parallel to the axis of the rotating barrel cam. This type of cam is often used to guide thread on sewing machines, looms and fabric making machines.

Fig. 5.12   A barrel or cylindrical cam

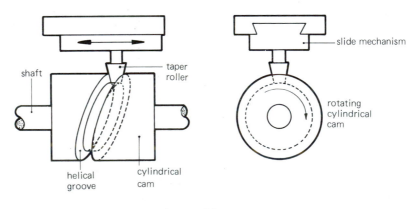

■ The Internal Combustion Engine

Motor vehicles use heat engines called **internal combustion engines**. Petrol and diesel engines are two similar internal combustion engines. Chemical energy enters these engines in the form of **fuel**, either petrol or diesel oil. The fuel is finely mixed with air in carefully controlled proportions. The fuel/air mixture is drawn into the **cylinder** through an inlet valve by downward movement of the **piston**. Upward movement of the piston compresses the fuel/air mixture into the **combustion chamber** (Fig. 5.13). An electric spark from the sparking plug causes the fuel to burn. Its chemical energy is transformed into heat energy which raises the temperature of the air in the cylinder. The temperature rise causes the pressure of the air to rise. The pressure of the air acting on the surface area of the piston creates a force which moves the piston down the cylinder. The movement of the piston is transmitted to whatever is connected to the engine, e.g. car wheels, generator, compressor. After the downward power stroke of the piston, the piston moves back up the cylinder driving the products of combustion past an exhaust valve and out of the cylinder.

The inlet and exhaust valves have to open and shut at just the right moment for effective operation of the engine.

Fig. 5.13   A section through the cylinder of a petrol engine

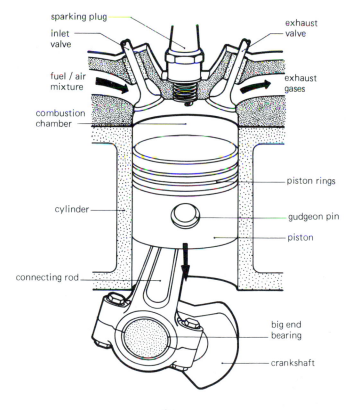

91

■ Engine Valve Operation

The valves used in motor vehicles are mushroom valves (Fig. 5.14). They are sometimes called **poppet valves**. The head of the valve rests in a conical seating machined in the cylinder head (Fig. 5.15). The valve seat and the seating in the cylinder head are ground to an angle of about 45° to ensure a good gas-tight seal.

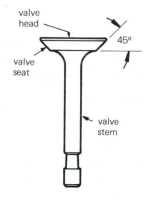

Fig. 5.14   A poppet valve

Fig. 5.15   Valve gear with rocker arm

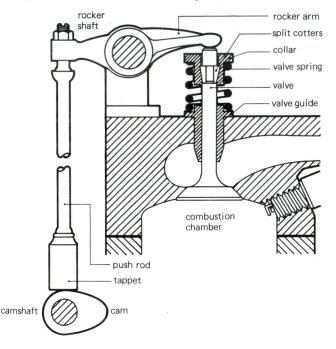

The valve stem slides in a renewable guide fixed in the cylinder head. The valve is held closed by a coil spring called the **valve spring** (Fig. 5.15). The spring is located on the cylinder head by the valve guide and by a collar attached to the valve stem. The collar is held in position by two split cotters which fit into a groove machined in the valve stem (Fig. 5.14).

The valves are opened by a cam mechanism (Fig. 5.15) and closed by the valve springs. The valve cams are fixed on a **camshaft** driven from the crankshaft by sprockets and a chain. As each cylinder has two valves, an inlet valve and an exhaust valve, there are two cams on the camshaft for each cylinder. A four-cylinder engine has eight cams on the camshaft (Fig. 5.16).

Fig. 5.16   The camshaft of a four-cylinder engine

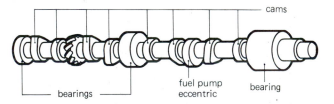

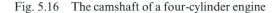

As the camshaft rotates, each cam lifts the follower in its guide. The cam follower is called a **tappet** (Figs. 5.15 and 5.17). The tappet motion is transmitted by a **push rod** to a lever called a **rocker arm**. The rocker arms are mounted on the cylinder head. Each cylinder has two rocker arms, one for each valve. They oscillate on a common **rocker shaft** (Fig. 5.17). The other end of the rocker arm presses down on the valve and causes it to open. When the tappet is on the crown of the cam, the push rod is lifted and the valve is held open. When the tappet is on the heel or dwell part of the cam, the valve spring holds the valve closed.

Each valve opens once for every two revolutions of the crankshaft. The camshaft is driven at half the speed of the crankshaft or engine speed. This is achieved by the crankshaft sprocket having half the number of teeth of the camshaft sprocket.

Fig. 5.17   A valve operating mechanism

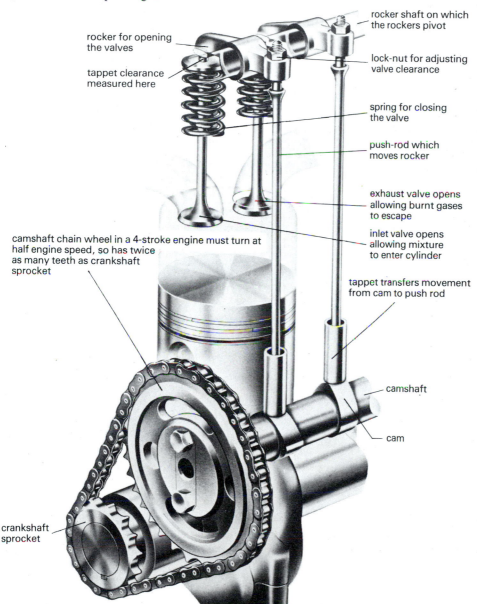

rocker for opening the valves

tappet clearance measured here

rocker shaft on which the rockers pivot

lock-nut for adjusting valve clearance

spring for closing the valve

push-rod which moves rocker

exhaust valve opens allowing burnt gases to escape

inlet valve opens allowing mixture to enter cylinder

camshaft chain wheel in a 4-stroke engine must turn at half engine speed, so has twice as many teeth as crankshaft sprocket

tappet transfers movement from cam to push rod

camshaft

cam

crankshaft sprocket

Fig. 5.18   An old industrial engine with a valve mechanism

Figure 5.18 shows an old stationary petrol engine with a single cylinder. Study the photograph carefully and identify the push rod, rocker arm, valve spring, tappet and cam.

☐ Other Valve Mechanism Designs

Many early motor cars had internal combustion engines with side valve mechanisms. The valve was opened by a cam on the camshaft, but the tappet lifted the valve directly (Fig. 5.19). This was a simple design which was cheap to produce.

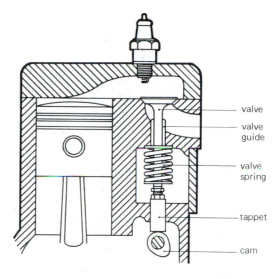

valve

valve guide

valve spring

tappet

cam

Fig. 5.19   A side valve mechanism

Some of the more powerful and larger petrol engines have camshafts above the cylinders and pistons. This type of camshaft is called an **overhead camshaft**. The cam operates the valve directly by use of a bucket tappet or a finger lever (Fig. 5.20).

Fig. 5.20   Overhead cam operating mechanisms

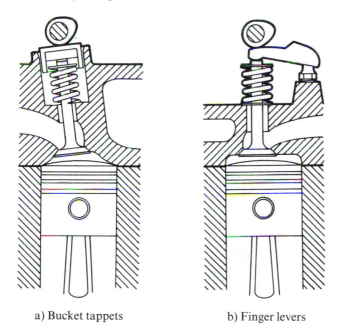

a) Bucket tappets   b) Finger levers

Overhead camshafts are usually driven by a toothed belt and toothed pulleys though they can be driven by chains and sprockets (Fig. 5.21). Figure 5.22 shows the Rover six-cylinder engine with an overhead camshaft. The camshaft is driven by a toothed belt. Rocker arms are used to operate the exhaust valves while the inlet valves are operated by bucket tappets (Fig. 5.23).

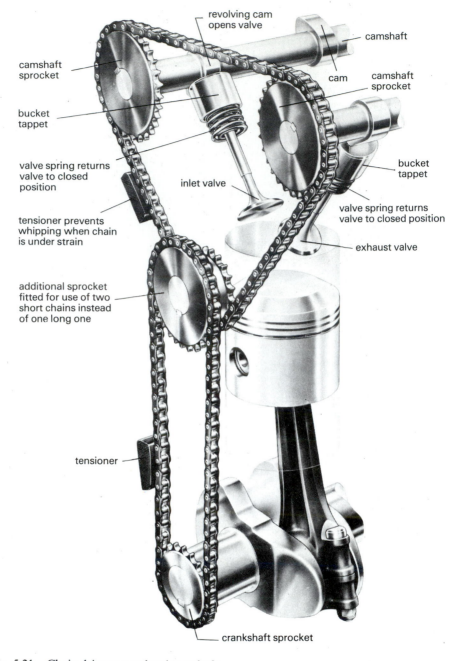

revolving cam
opens valve

camshaft

camshaft
sprocket

cam

camshaft
sprocket

bucket
tappet

bucket
tappet

valve spring returns
valve to closed
position

inlet valve

valve spring returns
valve to closed position

tensioner prevents
whipping when chain
is under strain

exhaust valve

additional sprocket
fitted for use of two
short chains instead
of one long one

tensioner

crankshaft sprocket

Fig. 5.21   Chain drive to overhead camshafts

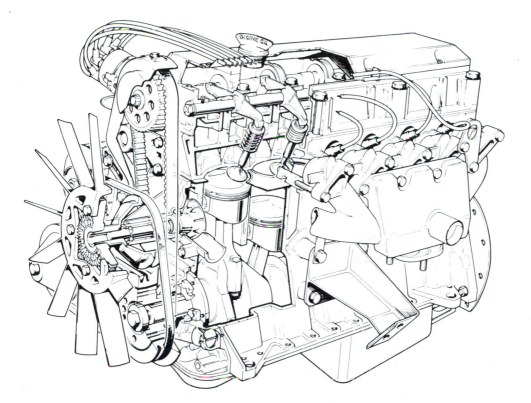

Fig. 5.22   The Rover engine – valve operating mechanism

Fig. 5.23   A section drawing of the Rover engine – overhead camshaft operating mechanism

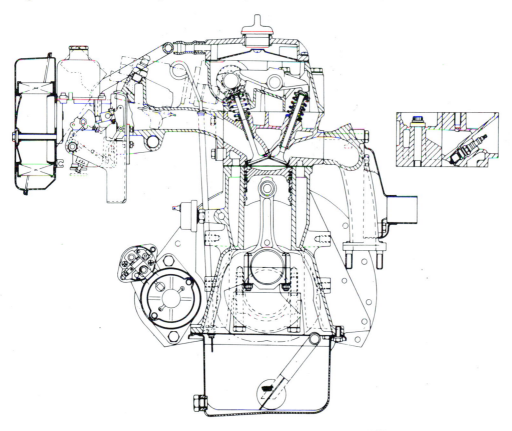

☐ Eccentrics

A circular cam is often called an **eccentric cam** because the axis of rotation of the cam is offset from the geometric centre of the circular disc (Fig. 5.24a). A concentric disc attached to a rotating shaft would have its axis of rotation coinciding with its geometric centre (Fig. 5.24b).

Fig. 5.24   a) An eccentric cam on a rotating shaft

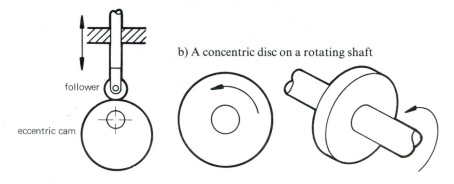

b) A concentric disc on a rotating shaft

An eccentric cam transmits simple harmonic motion to the follower. Examples of simple harmonic motion from everyday life are the up and down motion of a cork bobbing on the waves on a pond, and the oscillating motion of a pendulum weight as it swings from side to side (Fig. 5.25).

Fig. 5.25   Examples of simple harmonic motion

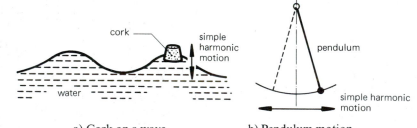

a) Cork on a wave   b) Pendulum motion

A graph of the follower motion gives the curve shown in Fig. 5.26. This shows follower displacement (distance moved by follower) plotted against the angle of rotation of the eccentric cam.

Fig. 5.26   Graph of follower motion for an eccentric cam

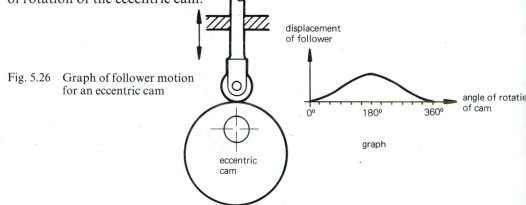

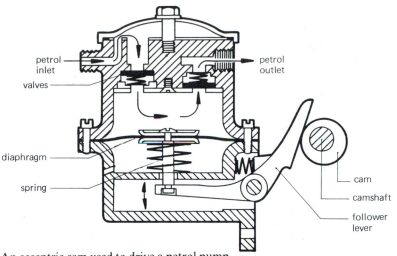

Fig. 5.27　An eccentric cam used to drive a petrol pump

An eccentric cam is used on the camshaft of a motorcar to drive the petrol pump (Fig. 5.27).

Eccentric cams are used to operate the valves of steam engines. An eccentric cam is attached to the crankshaft of the engine (Fig. 5.28a and b).

Fig. 5.28　a) A model steam engine　　　b) Eccentric cam used to operate the cylinder valve

■ Ratchet Mechanisms

A wheel with saw-shaped teeth round its rim is called a **ratchet**. The ratchet wheel usually engages with a tooth-shaped lever called a **pawl**. The purpose of a ratchet and pawl is to allow rotation in one direction only and prevent rotation in the opposite direction (Fig. 5.29).

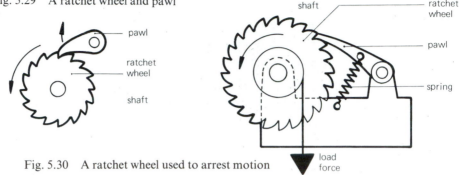

Fig. 5.29   A ratchet wheel and pawl

Fig. 5.30   A ratchet wheel used to arrest motion

A ratchet wheel can also be used to arrest motion. Figure 5.30 shows a ratchet wheel fixed to a shaft and winding drum. A rope is wound round the drum. Any load force applied to the rope is unable to unwind the drum because of the action of the ratchet and pawl. It is possible to wind up the rope because the ratchet can be rotated in an anticlockwise direction. Notice the pawl is held in position against the ratchet by a tension spring.

3   Name a woodworking tool that uses a ratchet.

A fishing reel uses a ratchet to prevent the fishing line unwinding. A fixed spool fishing reel contains two ratchet mechanisms. An extra ratchet is used on the line spool to tension the line when playing a fish (Fig. 5.31).

Fig. 5.31   a) A fishing reel ratchet mechanism   'b) A fixed spool ratchet mechanism

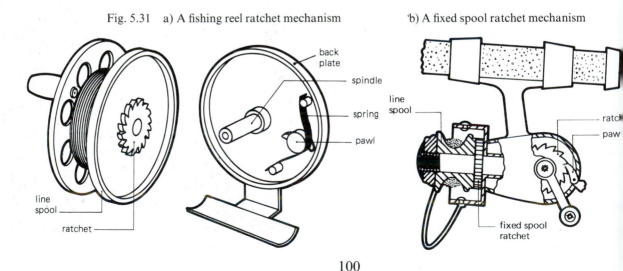

100

A crane winding mechanism makes use of a pawl and ratchet to allow rotary motion in one direction only. The crane winch can be wound up but the tension force in the cable cannot unwind the winch because of the ratchet mechanism (Fig. 5.32).

Fig. 5.32   Crane or winch – an example of a ratchet mechanism

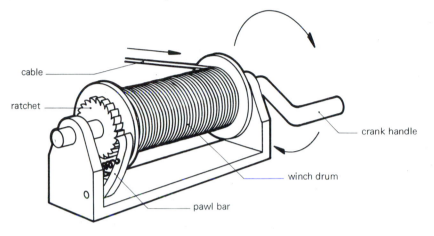

cable

ratchet

crank handle

winch drum

pawl bar

The ratchet wheel and pawl can be used in a different manner. The pawl is designed to rotate about the same centre as the ratchet wheel. An oscillating input motion is given to the pawl and it transmits motion to the ratchet wheel. The ratchet wheel is rotated in steps of one or more teeth by each input of motion from the pawl. A shaping machine uses this type of pawl and ratchet to advance the machine table. The pawl is given a reciprocating motion by a crank mechanism (Fig. 5.33a and b).

Fig. 5.33   a) A shaping machine ratchet mechanism   b)   The ratchet mechanism on a shaping machine

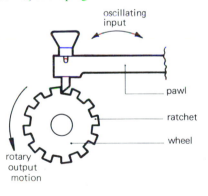

oscillating input

pawl

ratchet
wheel

rotary output motion

101

■ Construction Kits

MECCANO

The Meccano kit contains a **snail cam** (Fig. 5.34). The cam is fixed to an axle rod by a grub screw in the boss of the cam. A snail cam has a spiral profile and so gives a smooth rise motion to the follower. The radial notch in the cam causes a rapid return or fall of the follower.

Fig. 5.34   A snail cam

Fig. 5.35   The Meccano triple-throw eccentric

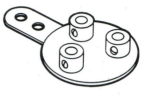

The Meccano kit also contains a triple-throw eccentric (Fig. 5.35).

Eccentric cams can be constructed from Meccano parts. For example, a bush wheel and pulley can be bolted together to make an eccentric cam (Fig. 5.36).

Fig. 5.36   An eccentric cam made from a bush wheel and pulley with a lever follower

The Meccano ratchet and pawl are shown in Fig. 5.37.

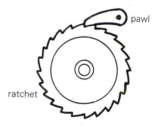

Fig. 5.37   The Meccano ratchet wheel and pawl

FISCHERTECHNIK

The Fischertechnik kit has two kinds of cam (Fig. 5.38).

Fig. 5.38   Fischertechnik cams

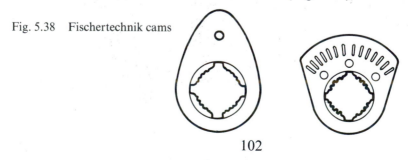

A number of ways of using the cams are shown in Fig. 5.39.

Fig. 5.39   Using the Fischertechnik cams

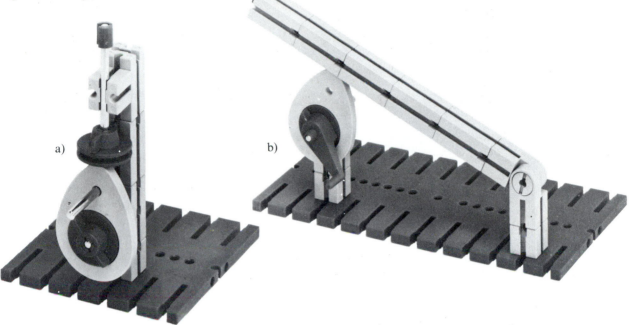

The Fischertechnik kit contains no purpose-made ratchet or pawl, but a gear can be used as a ratchet wheel. A triangular building block can be used as a pawl. Alternative ways of using the gear and triangular block are shown in Fig. 5.40.

Fig. 5.40 Using a Fischertechnik gear and triangular block as a ratchet wheel and pawl

a)

b)

c)

Answers to Questions
1 Internal combustion engine of a motorcar.
2 The valve is opening.
3 Woodwork ratchet brace or ratchet screwdriver.

6 Crank/Slider Mechanisms and Screw Mechanisms

Fig. 6.1   The inclined plane

■ The Inclined Plane

An **inclined plane** is a sloping surface used to gain mechanical advantage when raising a load (Fig. 6.1). Early man made use of the inclined plane to lift heavy blocks of stone. Huge stones were dragged up earth ramps and then carefully positioned on a stone structure. When the structure was complete, the earth ramp was removed.

1   Give an example of early man's use of the inclined plane.

The inclined plane is used today in many forms. For example, the slopes and ramps used in garages, on roads and on bridges make it easier for a motor to climb a height (Fig. 6.2a). The key used to secure a pulley or a gear on a shaft is another example of an inclined plane (Fig. 6.2b).

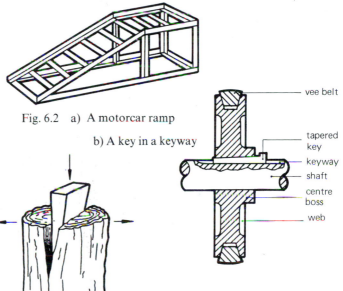

Fig. 6.2   a) A motorcar ramp

b) A key in a keyway

vee belt
tapered key
keyway
shaft
centre boss
web

Fig. 6.3   a) The wedge

b) Lifting a heavy load with a wedge   c) Cleaving apart the grain of a log with the wedge

The **wedge** is two inclined planes back-to-back. A wedge is often used to raise a heavy load through a small distance (Fig. 6.3b). For example, in a factory a wedge might be used to raise a heavy packing case sufficiently for the forks of a fork lift truck to get under it. The double inclined plane of the wedge is often used to cleave apart the fibres of a material. For example, a log can be split by driving a wedge along the wood grain (Fig. 6.3c).

The first tools were made by fixing wedge-shaped flint heads to wood or bone handles. These tools were used to hack, chop and cleave apart the fibres of materials ranging from timber to meat. Today, tools with a sharp cutting edge are usually made in wedge form. For example, wood chisels, knives, axes and lathe tools all make use of the wedge action (Fig. 6.4).

Fig. 6.4   a) An early tool (axe)   b) Chisel cutting action   c) Lathe tool bit cutting action

☐ The Mechanics of the Inclined Plane

It requires less effort to climb a gradual slope than a steep slope (Fig. 6.5).

Fig. 6.5   Climbing a slope

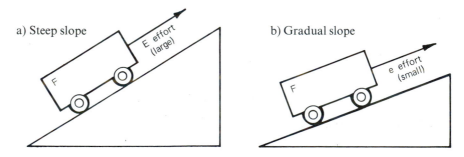

The effort required to pull a trolley up a slope depends on the angle of the inclined plane. A large effort is required for a steep slope. Less effort is required for a gradual slope (Fig. 6.6).

Fig. 6.6   Pulling a trolley up an inclined plane

a) Steep slope   E effort (large)   F   b) Gradual slope   e effort (small)   F

Consider a trolley being pulled up a slope (Fig. 6.7). The effort force required to move the trolley can be calculated if the dimensions of the slope are known.

Height of slope $= h$
Length of slope $= s$
Angle of slope $= \theta$
$\therefore \sin \theta = \dfrac{h}{s}$
Mass of trolley and load $= m$
Centre of gravity of the trolley is at G
Acceleration due to gravity $= g$

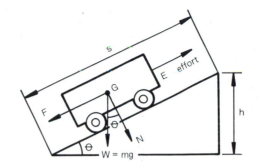

Fig. 6.7   Forces on a trolley on an inclined plane

The weight W of the trolley and its load is the force acting downwards towards the centre of the earth.

Weight $W = mg$

The weight of the trolley and its load can be broken down into two component forces at right angles to each other. One component force F acts down the slope and parallel to it.

Force $F = \text{weight} \times \sin \theta = W \sin \theta$

$F = mg \sin \theta.$

The other component force N acts perpendicular to the slope.

$N = mg \cos \theta.$

At the point when the trolley is just about to move up the slope, the effort force E balances the force F.

$E = F$

therefore $E = mg \sin \theta$

but $\sin \theta = h/s$

so effort force $E = \dfrac{mgh}{s}$ or $\dfrac{Wh}{s}.$

In practice, because of friction at the wheels, a force larger than $\dfrac{mgh}{s}$ is required to pull the trolley up the slope.

The velocity ratio of the inclined plane can be found from the formula:

$$\text{velocity ratio} = \frac{\text{distance moved by effort}}{\text{distance moved by load}}.$$

Therefore, velocity ratio $= \dfrac{s}{h}$.

Work done in raising load $=$ work done by the effort

$$\text{load} \times h = \text{effort} \times s.$$

Therefore, $\qquad \dfrac{\text{load}}{\text{effort}} = \dfrac{s}{h}.$

But mechanical advantage $= \dfrac{\text{load}}{\text{effort}}$

so the mechanical advantage of an inclined plane $= \dfrac{s}{h}$.

Example

a) What minimum effort force is required to pull a trolley weighing 1000 newtons up a slope of 1 in 100?

Fig. 6.8

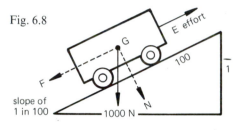

Resolving the components of the weight, force F down the slope $=$ weight $\times \sin \theta$

but weight $= 1000$ N and $\sin \theta = \dfrac{1}{100} = 0.01$.

Therefore, $F = 1000 \times \sin \theta$

$\qquad\qquad F = 1000 \times 0.01$

$\qquad\qquad F = 10$ N.

But $\qquad F = $ effort E.

Therefore, effort $= 10$ newtons.

b) What is the velocity ratio and mechanical advantage of this inclined plane?

$$\text{Velocity ratio} = \frac{\text{distance moved by effort}}{\text{distance moved by load}}$$

$$= \frac{100}{1}.$$

Therefore, $\qquad$ velocity ratio $= 100$.

$$\text{Mechanical advantage} = \frac{\text{load}}{\text{effort}} = \frac{s}{h} = \frac{1000}{10} = \frac{100}{1}.$$

Therefore, mechanical advantage $= 100$.

■ The Screw Thread

A **screw thread** is a helical or spiral groove cut in the surface of a cylindrical shaft. As the thread winds round the shaft, it moves along the shaft (Fig. 6.9a and b).

Fig. 6.9   a) A screw   b) The helix form

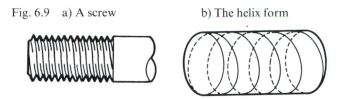

If an inclined plane is wrapped round a cylinder, its edge produces a **helix** form (Fig. 6.10). Thus a screw thread is only a disguised form of inclined plane.

Fig. 6.10   The inclined plane wrapped around a cylinder

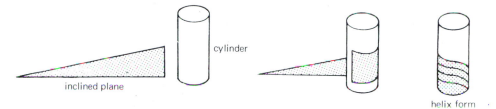

2   *Give examples of the use of the helix form.*

A screw is used to transmit motion and force. For example, the lead screw on a lathe transmits motion to the carriage in order to move the toolpost along the lathe bed (Fig. 6.11). In a screw-type nutcracker a screw thread is being used to transmit force (Fig. 6.12).

Fig. 6.11   Transmitting motion with a leadscrew on the lathe

Fig. 6.12   A nut-cracker screw used to transmit force

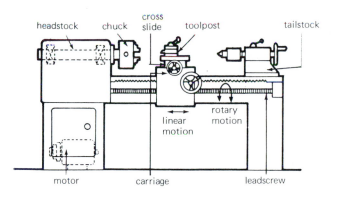

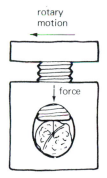

3   *Give examples of the use of screw threads.*

☐ Screw Thread Terms

Some of the terms associated with screw threads are shown in Fig. 6.13. The top of the thread is called the **crown**. The base of the thread is called the **root**. The **pitch** of a screw thread is the distance between the crown of one thread and the crown of the next thread.

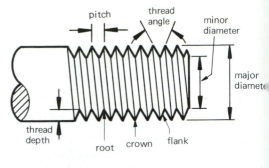

Fig. 6.13   Screw thread terms

A screw made with one helix or thread running round is a single start screw thread (Fig. 6.14a). A screw with more than one thread running round it is known as multiple start thread (Fig. 6.14b). Multiple start threads transmit more rapid motion.

Fig. 6.14   a) A single start thread   b) A multiple start thread (two start in this case)

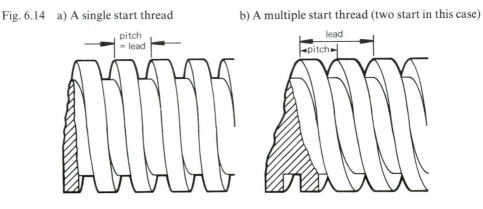

The distance a nut would move forward in one complete revolution of the screw shaft is called the **lead** (Fig. 6.14a and b). Lead = number of starts × pitch.

> 4   *For a single start thread, what is the connection between the pitch and the lead?*

■ Screw Thread Forms

Screw threads have two basic forms: the V-thread and the square thread (Fig. 6.15a and b). The **V-thread** gets its name from the vee-shaped groove of the thread form. A screw is used in a threaded or tapped hole or with a nut (Fig. 6.16a and b).

Fig. 6.15   a) V-thread   b) Square thread

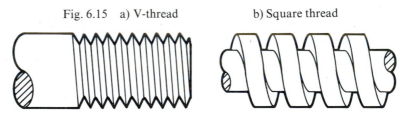

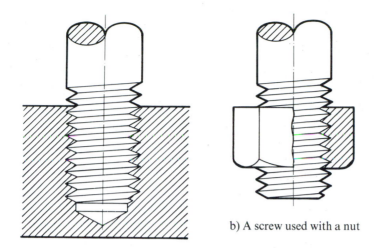

b) A screw used with a nut

Fig. 6.16   a) A screw in a tapped hole

Because of the large amount of friction between the sides or flanks of the screw and the nut, V-threads are used on fastening devices, e.g. set screws, nuts and bolts.

Before 1841 engineering firms used their own individual forms of screw thread. Then, Sir Joseph Whitworth, one of the pioneers of mechanical engineering, devised a standard form of screw thread. The British Standard Whitworth (BSW) screw thread has a thread angle of 55° (Fig. 6.17a). A slightly finer form of screwthread is the British Standard Fine (BSF). Electrical engineering industries have used the British Association (BA) thread (Fig. 6.17b). The Whitworth thread has been in use in British engineering industries until the recent change to the metric system.

The change to the metric system has meant that most of the wide range of threads have been replaced by the **ISO/metric thread**. The major diameter and pitch of a metric screw is measured in millimetres (Fig. 6.17c).

Fig. 6.17
a) British Standard Whitworth thread (BSW)   b) British Association thread (BA)   c) ISO/metric thread

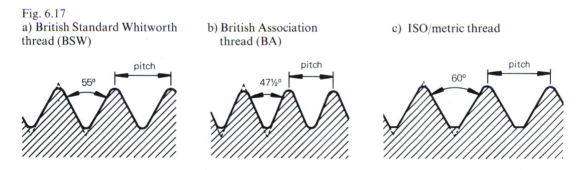

The **square thread** gets its name from the profile shape of the thread form (Fig. 6.18a). It is the thread most used for moving parts of machines, vice screws, lifting jacks and valve spindles. It is not as strong as the corresponding V-thread but friction is less.

111

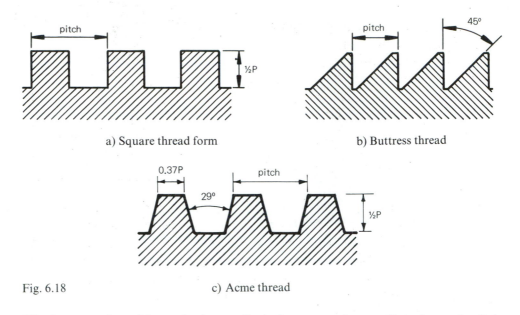

a) Square thread form

b) Buttress thread

Fig. 6.18

c) Acme thread

The **buttress thread** is used where a force has to act in one direction only. It is used in woodwork and other vices which are fitted with a quick acting mechanism.

The **acme thread** (Fig. 6.18c) is extensively used for transmitting motion in conjunction with a disengaging nut, as, for example, the lead screw of a lathe. The taper sides facilitate engagement of the nut with the screw. If wear takes place, adjustment is automatic by the nut moving deeper into engagement.

■ Screw Thread Applications

Cramps and vices make use of the square screw thread to tighten jaws which hold a workpiece firmly (Fig. 6.19a and b).

Fig. 6.19   Screw mechanisms

a) 'G' cramp   b) Metalwork vice

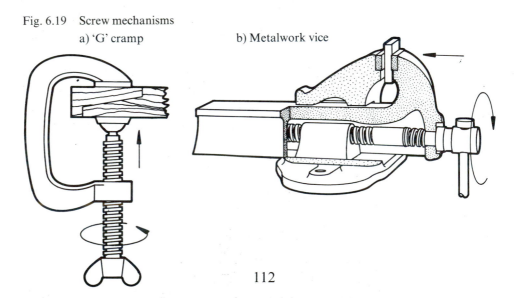

A screw thread can be used in the force transmitting mechanism of a press. A veneer or book-binding press (Fig. 6.20) uses a square thread. The force is transmitted downwards to squeeze the veneer flat. Fly presses use a similar screw mechanism.

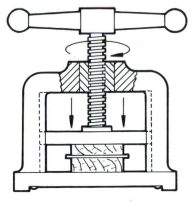

Fig. 6.20   A veneer press or book-binding press

Screw mechanisms are often used to enable heavy loads to be lifted. The screw jack shown (Fig. 6.21a) is used to raise heavy engineering components, e.g. to level a heavy casting on a machine table. Various types of screw jack are used to lift motor vehicles. One type of screw jack (Fig. 6.21b) fits into a recess in the chassis of a motorcar. The scissor type of screw jack (Fig. 6.21c) uses a parallelogram linkage to raise a car. It is placed under a chassis member and the screw is rotated to raise the vehicle.

Fig. 6.21

a) An engineering screw jack   b) A motor vehicle screw jack   d) A scissors screw jack

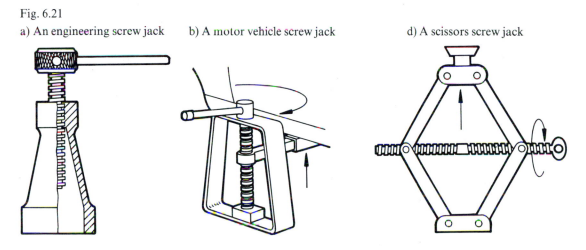

Square threads are often used on the leadscrews of machine tools (Fig. 6.22). On a milling machine, rotation of the leadscrew moves the machine table with linear motion. The leadscrew engages with a nut attached to the machine table. The table moves on a slideway. The leadscrew is turned by hand with a crank handle or by an electric motor.

Fig. 6.22   The leadscrew on the machine table of a milling machine

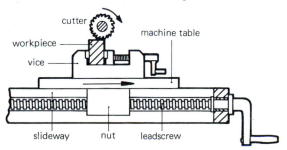

■ Crank Mechanisms

A **crank** is a device by which torque can be applied to a shaft. Figure 6.23 shows a simple crank handle.

The torque applied to the shaft = applied force × distance of force from axis.

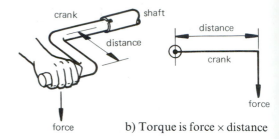

Fig. 6.23 a) A crank handle

b) Torque is force × distance

Figure 6.24a and b shows two forms of crank, the crank wheel and the crank handle.

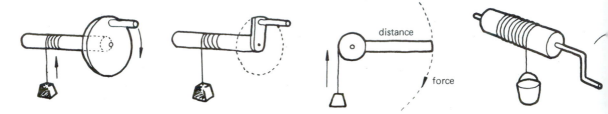

Fig. 6.24   a) The crank wheel   b) The crank handle   c) Torque applied by crank   d) The windlass

5   Give examples of the use of a crank handle or a crank wheel.

The windlass is an example of a crank handle (Fig. 6.24d). The Meccano and the Fischertechnik construction kits both have crank handles (Fig. 6.25).

Fig. 6.25   a) Meccano crank handles

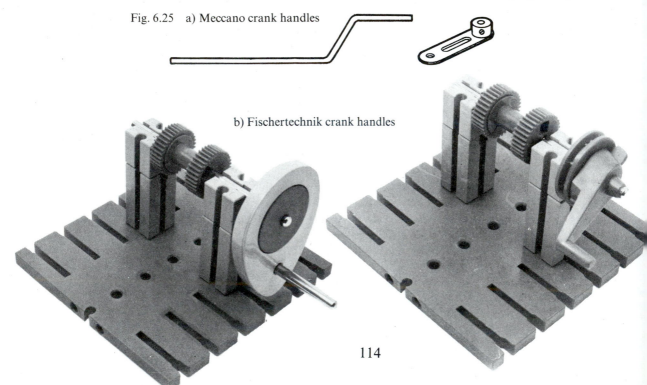

b) Fischertechnik crank handles

114

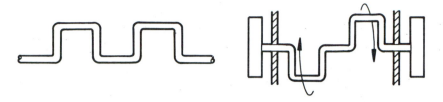

Fig. 6.26 a) A simple crankshaft   b) The crankshaft of a child's pedal car

A crank handle can be incorporated into a shaft. A shaft with several cranks in it is called a **crankshaft**. A simple crankshaft is shown in Fig. 6.26a.

    6   Name a woodworking tool that uses a crankshaft.

A child's pedal car uses a crankshaft to convert the torque applied by the child's legs into rotary motion which turns the wheels (Fig. 6.26b). A crankshaft is used in motor vehicle engines to transform the reciprocating motion of the pistons into rotary motion to drive the wheels (Fig. 6.27a). Each piston is attached to a crank of the crankshaft by a connecting rod (Fig. 6.27b). The crankshaft of an automobile engine is made of forged steel or cast in a special quality cast iron. The webs or cranks which join the crank pins are carefully shaped to act as balance weights to ensure smooth running.

Fig. 6.27 a) The crankshaft of an automobile engine

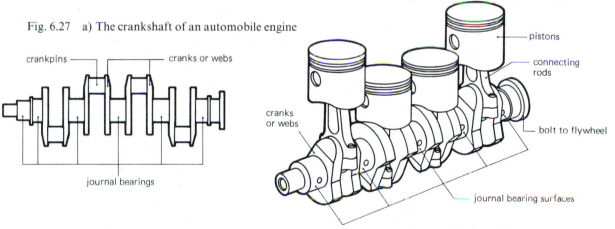

b) A four-cylinder engine crankshaft, connecting rods and pistons

■ Crank/Slider Mechanisms

A crankshaft, connecting rod and piston in a cylinder is an example of a crank/slider mechanism. The crank/slider mechanism consists of a rotating crank which is connected to a slider by a connecting rod (Fig. 6.28).

Fig. 6.28 A crank/slider mechanism

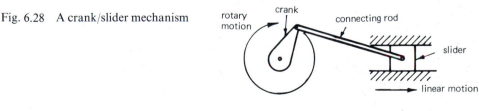

115

In the crank/slider mechanism, freely moving joints linking the crank and connecting rod, and the slider and the connecting rod are necessary. The mechanism can be used to convert rotary motion into reciprocating motion. For example, a compressor uses an electric motor or an internal combustion engine to provide a rotary motion input. A crank/slider mechanism receiving this input makes a piston move with reciprocating motion to compress the air in the cylinder of the compressor.

The crank/slider mechanism can also be used to convert reciprocating motion into rotary motion. The internal combustion engine and the steam engine are examples of this form of motion conversion.

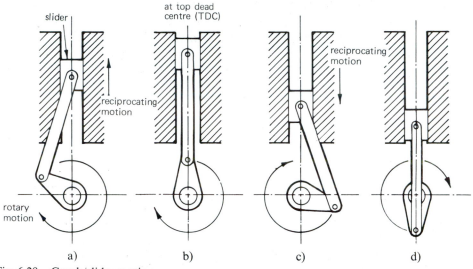

Fig. 6.29   Crank/slider motion

In Fig. 6.29, the crank moves with rotary motion and the slider moves with reciprocating motion (Fig. 6.29a). When the slider reaches the top extreme of its motion, it is at its **top dead centre** (Fig. 6.29b). The velocity of the slider at the instant it reaches top dead centre is zero. When the slider reaches the lower extreme of its motion, it is at its **bottom dead centre** (Fig. 6.29d). The distance the slider moves between top and bottom dead centre is called the **stroke**.

7   What is the instantaneous velocity of the slider at bottom dead centre?

■ **Crank/Slider Mechanism Applications**

1   A FABRIC TESTER

When the crank of a crank/slider mechanism is given continuous rotary motion, the slider moves with reciprocating motion (Fig. 6.30a). This property can be used in a fabric testing machine (Fig. 6.30b). The machine tests the wear properties of different fabrics. A wire brush, like a file card, is attached to the

116

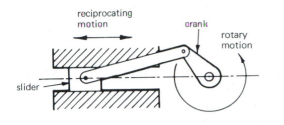
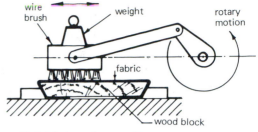

Fig. 6.30

a) The crank/slider mechanism – reciprocating motion   b) A fabric testing machine

slider end of the connecting rod. Samples of fabric are clamped under the wire brush. The crank is rotated by an electric motor. The wire brush reciprocates backwards and forwards on the sample of fabric until it wears through the material. A fabric tester made by a pupil is shown in Fig. 6.31a. The number of revolutions of the crank wheel are recorded on an electromagnetic counter. One method of operating this is by a cam attached to the crank wheel. The cam operates a microswitch once on each revolution (Fig. 6.31b).

Fig. 6.31   a) Pupil's project – a fabric testing machine

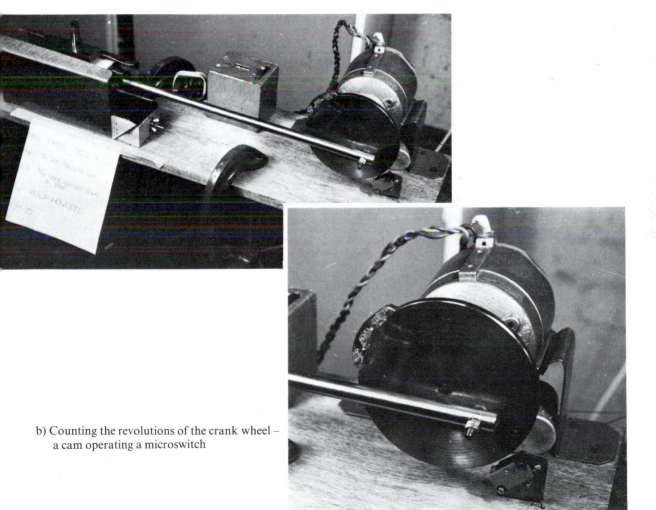

b) Counting the revolutions of the crank wheel –
   a cam operating a microswitch

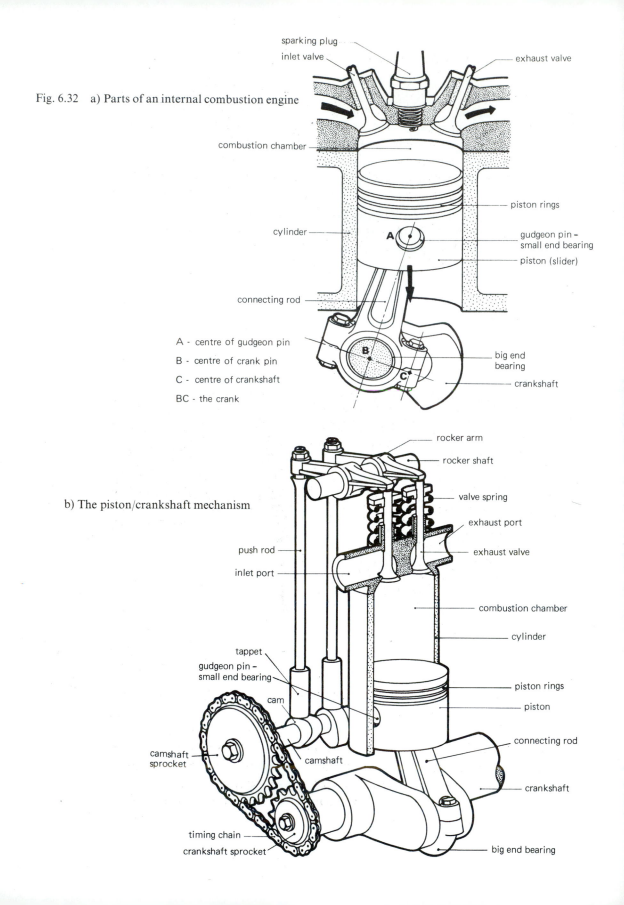

sparking plug

inlet valve

exhaust valve

Fig. 6.32   a) Parts of an internal combustion engine

combustion chamber

cylinder

piston rings

gudgeon pin – small end bearing

piston (slider)

A

connecting rod

A - centre of gudgeon pin

B - centre of crank pin

C - centre of crankshaft

BC - the crank

B

C

big end bearing

crankshaft

rocker arm

rocker shaft

b) The piston/crankshaft mechanism

valve spring

exhaust port

push rod

exhaust valve

inlet port

combustion chamber

cylinder

tappet

gudgeon pin – small end bearing

cam

piston rings

piston

camshaft sprocket

camshaft

connecting rod

crankshaft

timing chain

crankshaft sprocket

big end bearing

2 THE INTERNAL COMBUSTION ENGINE

The internal combustion engine is an example of the use of the crank/slider mechanism. The slider is the **piston**. It can move up and down in a **cylinder** (Fig. 6.32). The crankshaft and the piston are joined by a **connecting rod**. The connecting rod has bearings at each end. The small end of the connecting rod is fixed to the piston by a **gudgeon pin**. The gudgeon pin can rotate freely in the connecting rod in the **small end bearing**. The connecting rod is fixed at the large end to the crankshaft. It can rotate freely on the crankshaft in the **big end bearing**. Pressure acting on the surface area of the piston creates a force which moves the piston downwards. The pressure is caused by the working fluid (air) being heated to a high temperature by the burnt fuel. The downward force on the piston produces linear motion. This is transformed into rotary motion by the crankshaft.

3 STEAM ENGINES

Steam engines are external combustion engines. The chemical energy of the fuel is transformed into heat energy outside the cylinder.

Fig. 6.33   A small steam locomotive

Figure 6.33 shows a small steam locomotive made by a pupil. Steam engines are another example of the use of the crank/slider mechanism. Figure 6.34 shows a small oscillating steam engine often made in school workshops.

The steam from an inlet pipe passes through a port and enters the cylinder. The pressure of the steam acting on the surface area of the piston creates a force which moves the piston downwards. The force is transmitted by a connecting rod to a crank wheel attached to the crankshaft. Here, the linear motion of the

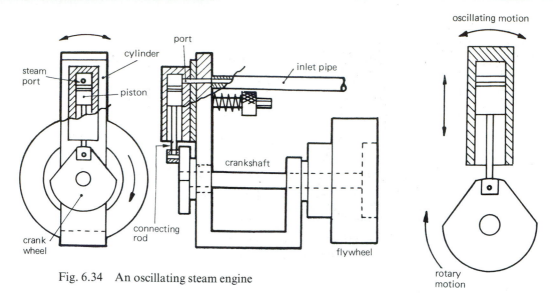

Fig. 6.34   An oscillating steam engine

piston is transformed into rotary motion of the crank wheel. The cylinder of this type of steam engine is pivoted. This allows the mechanism to operate without a little end bearing. In operation, the cylinder oscillates about its pivot, hence the name, an oscillating steam engine. Steam exhausts from the cylinder through an exhaust port which is uncovered at one point in the cylinder's oscillation. The inlet port is uncovered at a different point in the cylinder's oscillation.

A flywheel is attached to the crankshaft. The mass of the flywheel is spread round its circumference. Once the flywheel is in motion, its kinetic energy (energy of motion) tends to keep it rotating. The flywheel action results in a smooth, continuous output motion from the engine even though the energy input to the engine is pulsating.

Figure 6.35 shows a steam engine with a cast flywheel. Notice how the mass of the flywheel is spread around its outside rim.

Fig. 6.35   a) A double acting steam engine   b) The use of a flywheel

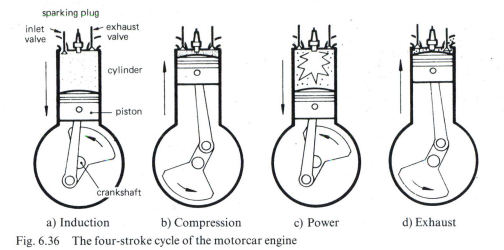

| a) Induction | b) Compression | c) Power | d) Exhaust |

Fig. 6.36   The four-stroke cycle of the motorcar engine

☐ The Four-stroke Cycle

The internal combustion engine used in most motorcars operates in a constantly repeated four-stroke cycle. Each stroke is shown in Fig. 6.36.

INDUCTION STROKE

The exhaust valve is closed and the inlet valve is open. As the piston moves down the cylinder, it creates a partial vacuum in the cylinder. As gas pressure in the inlet valve pipe is greater than that in the cylinder, an air and petrol mixture is induced into the cylinder.

COMPRESSION STROKE

The inlet and the exhaust valves are closed. The piston moves up the cylinder. The air and petrol mixture is compressed to about one-seventh of its original volume. The pressure rises to about eight atmospheres.

POWER STROKE

At the end of the compression stroke, the mixture of petrol and air is ignited by an electric spark from the sparking plug. Rapid combustion of the mixture occurs. This causes a very rapid rise in temperature and pressure to about thirty-five atmospheres. The pressure acts on the surface area of the piston crown causing a force. The force pushes the piston downwards. Therefore, work is done in moving both the parts of the engine and whatever is coupled to the engine. Both valves are still closed.

EXHAUST STROKE

The exhaust valve is open and the inlet valve is closed. The piston moves up the cylinder and drives the exhaust gases out through the exhaust valve. They pass through the exhaust pipe and silencer to the atmosphere.

This cycle of four strokes requires two complete revolutions of the crankshaft.

■ The Crank and Slotted Lever Mechanism

This mechanism (Fig. 6.37) is used on machine tools like the shaper and on special kinds of grinder. It enables a cutting tool to move forward slowly across the metal workpiece. After a slow, powerful cutting stroke, the toolpost ram returns quickly, ready for the next stroke.

The quick return mechanism consists of a slotted lever arm pivoted at its base (Fig. 6.37). It is linked by a peg to a bull gear. This is a large gear ring driven by a pinion on an electric motor (Fig. 6.39). The slotted arm is also connected to a

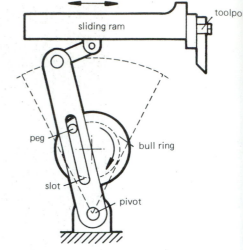

Fig. 6.37   The crank and slotted lever mechanism

sliding ram which carries the toolpost and cutting tool. The motion of the bull ring is converted into the reciprocating motion of the sliding ram.

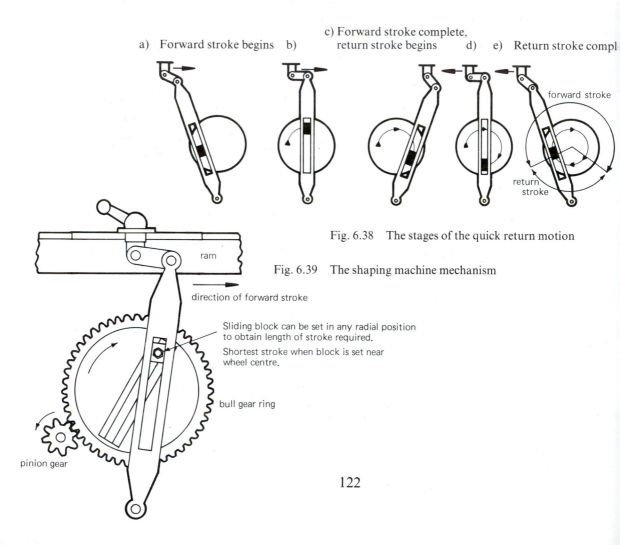

a)   Forward stroke begins   b)

c) Forward stroke complete, return stroke begins   d)   e)   Return stroke complete

Fig. 6.38   The stages of the quick return motion

Fig. 6.39   The shaping machine mechanism

direction of forward stroke

Sliding block can be set in any radial position to obtain length of stroke required.
Shortest stroke when block is set near wheel centre.

bull gear ring

pinion gear

122

Fig. 6.40   The shaping machine

The five stages of the quick return mechanism motion are shown in Fig. 6.38. On a shaping machine (Fig. 6.40) the length of the cutting stroke can be adjusted. Figure 6.39 shows a quick return mechanism with a sliding block which can be re-positioned to adjust the length of stroke.

Answers to Questions
1   Stonehenge, the Egyptian pyramids.
2   Helter-skelter at a fairground, mincing machine in the kitchen, Archimedes' water-raising screw.
3   Nuts and bolts, set screws, vices, cramps, car jacks, MES torch lightbulbs, corkscrews.
4   The pitch and the lead are equal on a single start thread.
5   Mincing machine, rotary egg whisk, crank handle on a motor car, washing mangle, crank handles on machine vices and feeds on machine tools.
6   Woodwork brace.
7   Zero.

7 Couplings and Shafts

■ Couplings

A **coupling** is a joint connecting two shafts to enable motion and torque to be transmitted from one shaft to another.

■ Aligned Shafts

Shafts that are in line are called **aligned shafts**. A flanged coupling, split sleeve or muff coupling is used to connect aligned shafts (Fig. 7.1). Figure 7.1 also shows how the bolt heads and nuts are prevented from projecting and causing danger. The flanged coupling and the muff coupling are examples of a **rigid coupling**. In each case the shafts are fixed to the coupling by means of a key and keyway.

Fig. 7.1   a) A flanged coupling   b) A muff or split coupling

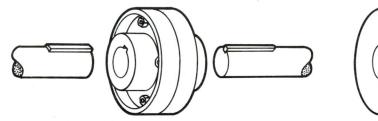

■ Flexible Couplings

Flexible couplings are used when the shafts intersect at a slight angle. They are also used when it is desired to damp down any vibrations to which a shaft is subjected, or to reduce shocks (Fig. 7.2).

Fig. 7.2   A flexible coupling   Fig. 7.3   A rubber trunnion coupling

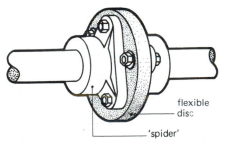

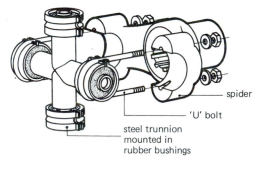

124

The joint is constructed from a disc of rubberised fabric connected between two 'spiders'. Flexing of the fabric allows for the variation in angle between the two shafts. This joint is cheap to produce and requires no lubrication. However, the maximum angle of drive at which it can operate is small. It will not transmit a high torque. It also sometimes fails to maintain shaft alignment. A flexible coupling of this type can easily be made in the school workshop. Two Meccano bush wheels with a thick rubber sheet between them can be used to act as a flexible coupling. Many motorcars use flexible couplings in the steering column.

Where it is necessary to transmit high torque through two shafts at an angle, e.g. vehicle transmission systems, a **rubber trunnion** is sometimes used. This is a steel trunnion or cross mounted in especially moulded rubber bushings (Fig. 7.3). Figure 7.4 shows an alternative flexible joint commonly called a rubber doughnut coupling.

Fig. 7.4   A rubber doughnut flexible coupling

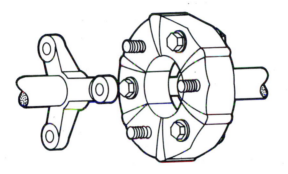

■ Universal Joints

Angular movement between two shafts can be achieved by the use of a **universal joint** (**UJ**). The simplest form of universal joint is the flexible disc already mentioned. Another type is the **Hooke's joint** (Fig. 7.5). This consists of two yokes, one attached to each shaft, and a cross-shaped centre piece on which the yokes pivot. The basic design may be modified for greater efficiency by the fitting of roller bearings and passages for lubrication (Fig. 7.6).

Fig. 7.5   A Hooke's type universal joint   Fig. 7.6   A motorcar propeller shaft universal joint

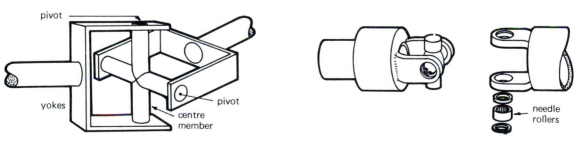

Another form of universal joint is based on the ball and socket principle (Fig. 7.7). The joint is precision made and is frequently used for machine tool drives. A spanner socket set universal joint allows nuts in inaccessible places to be tightened.

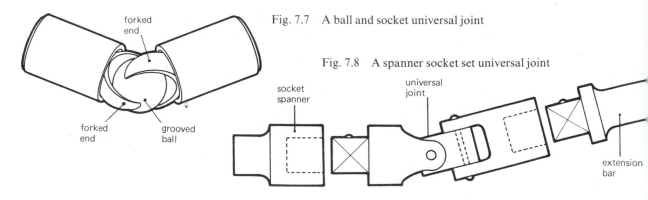

forked
end

forked
end

grooved
ball

Fig. 7.7   A ball and socket universal joint

Fig. 7.8   A spanner socket set universal joint

socket
spanner

universal
joint

extension
bar

Fig. 7.9   A Hooke's joint used on a tractor steering column

Universal joints are compact, efficient and suitable for high rotational speeds. They can connect shafts out of alignment by up to 20°. There is one disadvantage. When this type of joint is used to transmit drive through an angle, the output shaft does not rotate at a constant speed. During the first 90° of its motion, the output shaft travels faster than the input shaft and on the second 90°, slower. Using two joints, it is possible to cause the variation in speed set up by one joint to cancel out that in the other. It is important that both driver and driven shafts are at the same angle to the intermediate shaft and that the yokes are in the same plane (Fig. 7.10).

126

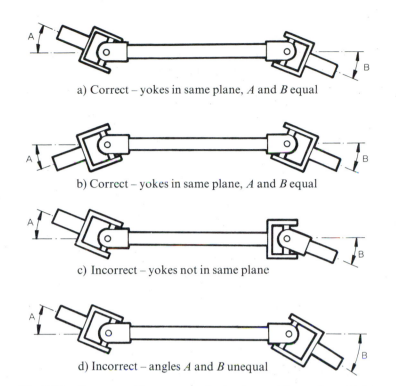

a) Correct – yokes in same plane, A and B equal

b) Correct – yokes in same plane, A and B equal

c) Incorrect – yokes not in same plane

d) Incorrect – angles A and B unequal

Fig. 7.10   Correct and incorrect methods of assembling universal joints

When the shafts are too short to allow the use of two joints, a special double universal joint may be used. This will allow for angular contact between the shafts and a constant speed of the driven shaft.

☐ Constant Velocity Joints

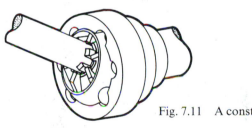

Fig. 7.11   A constant velocity joint

Where drive has to be transmitted through a large angle and it is impossible to obey the rules shown in Fig. 7.10, a **constant velocity (CV) joint** can be used (Fig. 7.11).

This allows the driven shaft to rotate at a constant speed even if there are frequent angular changes. A typical application is on a front wheel drive vehicle (Fig. 7.12). If a constant velocity joint was not used, there would be considerable vibration due to variations of speed.

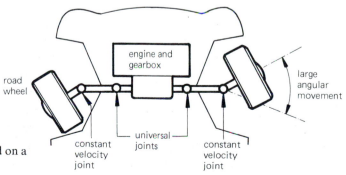

Fig. 7.12   Constant velocity joints as used on a British Leyland Mini

127

■ Sliding Couplings

A **sliding coupling** is one which allows a shaft to slide axially while still transmitting rotary motion (Fig. 7.13).

Fig. 7.13   A sliding coupling

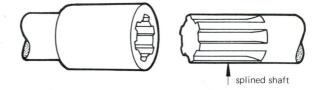

splined shaft

This is achieved by using a **splined shaft**. The keys machined on the shaft mate with slots in the coupling. They are not a tight fit but there should be no slackness. This method is often used on motor vehicle transmission systems and also machine tool power drives.

■ Simple Couplings

The following drive couplings may be useful in projects, or when you are working with construction kits.

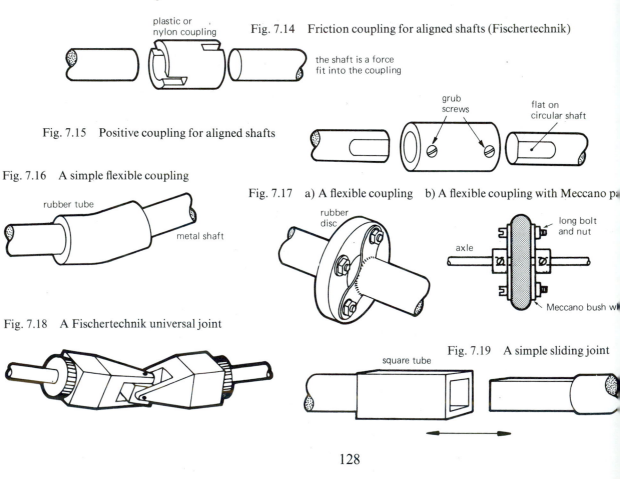

plastic or nylon coupling

Fig. 7.14   Friction coupling for aligned shafts (Fischertechnik)

the shaft is a force fit into the coupling

grub screws

flat on circular shaft

Fig. 7.15   Positive coupling for aligned shafts

Fig. 7.16   A simple flexible coupling

Fig. 7.17   a) A flexible coupling   b) A flexible coupling with Meccano pa

rubber tube

metal shaft

rubber disc

long bolt and nut

axle

Meccano bush w

Fig. 7.18   A Fischertechnik universal joint

Fig. 7.19   A simple sliding joint

square tube

8 Friction~Brakes and Clutches

Fig. 8.1 Pulling a sleigh over rough ground

■ Introduction

Friction is the name given to the force which tends to prevent sliding between surfaces in contact. If the surfaces are clean and dry, the force needed to overcome friction depends upon:
a) the materials from which the surfaces are made;
b) the surface finish, i.e. rough, smooth or polished;
c) the force pressing the surfaces together.

> *In Fig. 8.1, the horse is unable to pull the sleigh over the rough ground. Suggest a more effective way of overcoming the problem of moving the sleigh.*

■ The Coefficient of Friction

When a rough surface tries to slide over another rough surface, the force of friction opposes the movement. The maximum force of friction that just prevents movement is called the **force of limiting friction**. This limiting friction force is proportional to the force pressing the surfaces together.

Imagine a block resting on rough ground (Fig. 8.2). The two surfaces in contact are being pressed together by the weight of the block W acting at right angles to the two surfaces in contact. By Newton's Third Law of action and reaction, a contact force N (equal to W) opposes this weight force. A gradually increasing force P is applied to the block. For small values

Fig. 8.2 A block resting on rough ground

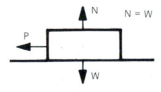

129

of P there is no sliding. At the point when sliding is just about to occur, the force P is at its maximum value. The block is in equilibrium just before it slides, and the force of friction equals the maximum applied force (Fig. 8.3).

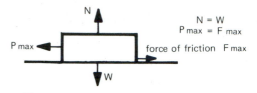

Fig. 8.3   The limiting friction force

Investigation shows that at this point the ratio $\dfrac{F_{max}}{N}$ is a constant. We call this contact the **coefficient of friction,** μ.

$$\mu = \frac{F_{max}}{N} \left(= \frac{P_{max}}{W} \right)$$

•or $F_{max} = \mu N$

where N is the force at right angles to the two surfaces in contact (pushing them together), and F_{max} is the force of limiting friction. The lower the value of μ, the more easily surfaces will slip over one another. The table gives values of the coefficient of friction for different surfaces in contact.

Material	μ
Wood on wood (dry)	0.25–0.5
Metal on wood (dry)	0.2 –0.6
Metal on metal (dry)	0.15–0.3
Metal on metal (oiled)	0.07–0.08
Clutch lining	0.3 –0.55

The higher the number, the greater the resistance to sliding. Also notice that investigation shows the coefficient of friction is not affected by the areas of the surfaces in contact.

☐ Examples of Friction Problems

The force of limiting friction equals the coefficient of friction multiplied by the normal force pressing the surfaces together.

$$F_{max} = \mu N.$$

Example 1
A block of metal weighing 100 newtons is resting on a horizontal metal surface. The coefficient of friction between the metal surfaces is 0.2. What force is required to move the block?

Fig. 8.4

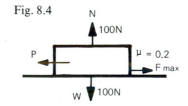

The normal force N pressing the surfaces together equals the weight of the block (100 N).

Using $F_{max} = \mu N$

$$F_{max} = 0.2 \times 100$$
$$= 20 \text{ newtons.}$$

But the force P required to move the block is equal to the force of limiting friction F_{max}.

Therefore a force of 20 newtons is required to move the block.

Example 2
A wooden crate weighing 3000 newtons rests on a horizontal wooden floor. A force of 900 newtons is required to just make the crate slide. What is the coefficient of friction for wood on wood in this example?

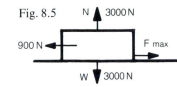

Fig. 8.5

The force of limiting friction F_{max} is equal to the applied force, 900 newtons.

The normal force N, pressing the two surfaces together, is equal to the weight of 3000 newtons.

Using $\mu = \dfrac{F_{max}}{N}$.

$$\mu = \dfrac{900}{3000}$$
$$= 0.3.$$

Therefore the coefficient of friction for wood on wood is 0.3.

■ Static Friction

Just before sliding occurs, the friction force is a maximum and is called the **limiting friction**. Before sliding occurs, the force trying to cause sliding and the friction force remain equal to each other. This is a case of **static friction**.

■ Dynamic Friction

When limiting friction has been exceeded and movement occurs between the surfaces, the friction force required to maintain movement is less than the static friction. This is called **dynamic friction**. The friction force now does work since movement is taking place (remember, work = force × distance moved), and heat is produced at the surfaces.

Fig. 8.6   Without friction we could not walk, tyres would not grip and brakes would not work

■ Uses of Friction

Friction enables us to move forward by walking, and to warm our hands by rubbing them together. Friction keeps nuts and bolts done up and prevents articles from sliding around in a moving vehicle. Friction enables clutch and brake linings to transmit forces and tyres to grip the road. However, friction between contacting surfaces is often a disadvantage because it produces heat and wear. Friction can be reduced by the use of better bearings and lubrication.

Fig. 8.7   A great deal of energy is converted quickly when a vehicle is brought to rest

■ Brakes

A moving vehicle possesses energy of motion (called kinetic energy). This must be converted into some other form of energy if the vehicle is to be brought to rest.

The speed of energy conversion governs how quickly a vehicle can stop. Most braking systems convert energy of motion into heat energy. The heat energy is transmitted to the air flowing over the brake. If the brake itself becomes too hot, it is inclined to **'fade'** (i.e. to lose its efficiency). This is dangerous if it happens on a motor vehicle, so designers always ensure there is adequate brake cooling.

132

Fig. 8.8   Most braking systems convert energy of motion into heat

Figure 8.8 shows a very simple brake. A lever is used to press a brake block on to the rim of a carriage wheel. Figures 8.9 to 8.12 are examples of simple brakes. A steel-band brake (Fig. 8.10) is an externally contracting brake often used on lifting and winding mechanisms.

Fig. 8.9   A cantilever-action bicycle caliper brake

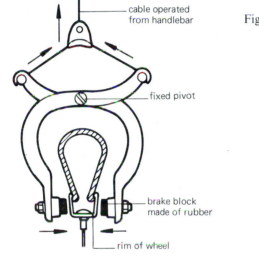

Fig. 8.10   A steel-band brake

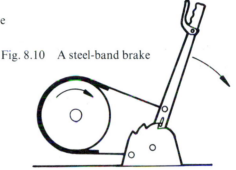

Fig. 8.12   A mechanically operated disc brake on a kart

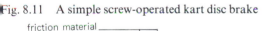

Fig. 8.11   A simple screw-operated kart disc brake

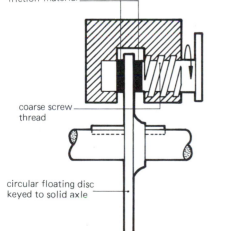

■ Motor Vehicle Brakes

To obtain maximum braking efficiency, all wheels should have brakes and each wheel should be held so that its tyre is on the verge of skidding.

If sufficient effort is available to lock the wheels, friction between the tyre and the road surface is the main factor governing braking. This is why vehicle stopping distances are increased in icy conditions – because there is less friction between the tyre and road surface.

■ Drum Brakes

The internally expanding shoe brake (Fig. 8.13) is in common use. Each shoe has a replaceable asbestos-based friction lining riveted or bonded to it. By means of a lever operated cam, the shoes are forced outwards (expanded) inside a cast iron drum which revolves with the wheels. The spring pulls the shoes together after the brakes have been released. Rotation of the drum in the direction shown in Fig. 8.13 tends to push shoe *A* harder into contact and tends to push shoe *B* to the 'off' position. Shoe *A* is called the leading shoe and is responsible for most of the braking effect. Shoe *B* is called the trailing shoe; it has less effect and less wear. This type of brake is called a single leading shoe **drum brake**. Many brakes have two leading shoes for greater efficiency.

Fig. 8.13   A mechanically operated drum brake

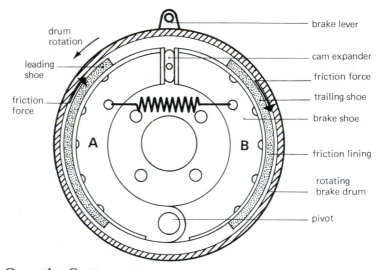

☐ Brake Operating Systems

Brakes can be operated in many ways.

1 MECHANICAL BRAKES

Rods, cables and levers are often used to operate the relatively simple braking systems to be found on pedestrian controlled trolleys, large lathes, bicycles and motorcycles. Where a number of brakes need to be operated simultaneously, for example on a motorcar, the mechanical linkages tend to be complicated and require frequent adjustment by skilled mechanics.

2 HYDRAULIC BRAKES

This is a highly efficient system which is suited to vehicles having independent suspension systems. Figure 8.14 shows the foot brake acting on a master cylinder. This supplies fluid to the various wheel cylinders. When a force is applied to the foot pedal, each brake works at the same time. Braking throws the weight of a vehicle forward on to the front wheels. Because of this, greater braking power is possible on the front wheels compared with the back wheels. On most vehicles, advantage is taken of this greater braking power at the front wheels by increasing the area of the front brake cylinder pistons and by fitting larger brakes.

Fig. 8.14 A hydraulic brake system

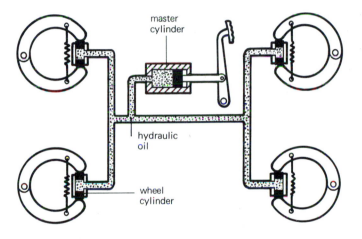

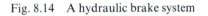

Fig. 8.15   A twin (two) leading shoe brake

The brake shoes of a twin leading shoe brake are operated by their own hydraulic cylinders which are connected to a master cylinder (Fig. 8.15).

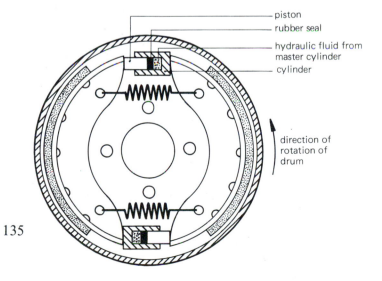

135

As brake fluid cannot be compressed it is able to transmit movement. Air is compressible. If any air is present in the system the pedal may feel spongy. This air must be removed by a process called **'bleeding'**.

If there is a break or leak in the hydraulic system, all braking power is lost. Some vehicles have a dual-hydraulic system as an added safety measure.

It is a legal requirement that motor vehicles have a mechanical brake to lock two wheels when it is parked. The mechanical brake is usually operated by a hand lever. The mechanical brake acts as a safety measure should the hydraulic brakes fail in use.

Drum brakes do not easily dissipate generated heat to the air so many modern vehicles are fitted with disc brakes.

3 DISC BRAKES

All **disc brakes** have a metal disc attached to the hub or axle of the rotating wheel. When the brake is applied, a caliper grips the rotating disc. Figure 8.16 shows the principle of a hydraulically operated brake.

A **hydraulic disc brake** has a cast iron disc sandwiched between two pads, which are lined with asbestos-based material. The pads are pressed against the disc by a hydraulic system. On four-wheeled vehicles, this system usually includes a vacuum servo unit to boost the driver's effort. Disc brakes are fully exposed to the air and dissipate heat easily.

Fig. 8.16   How a motorcycle disc brake works

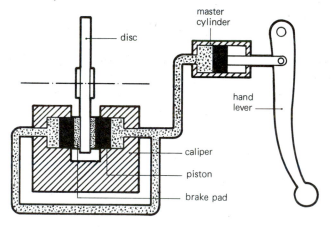

The hydraulic kart disc brake shown in Fig. 8.17 has a master cylinder, fluid reservoir and flexible hydraulic tube connected to the disc caliper.

Advantages of disc brakes
a) Good heat dissipation and little tendency to brake fade. They are more effective than drum brakes.
b) The pads are self adjusting. They are easily inspected for wear and can be quickly changed when worn.

136

Fig. 8.17   A hydraulic kart disc brake

One disadvantage is the difficulty of fitting an efficient mechanical handbrake for parking purposes. For this reason, and because greater stopping power is required at the front of a vehicle, a very popular braking arrangement consists of disc brakes for the front wheels and drum brakes at the rear wheels.

■ Clutches

A **clutch** is a device for enabling a rotating shaft to be easily connected to or disconnected from a second shaft. The two shafts must be in line. The two main types are the positive clutch and the friction clutch.

■ Positive Clutches

Positive clutches are normally used only if the driving shaft can be brought to rest before engaging the clutch. There are claws on the driver and driven clutch plates. These mesh with each other and are pressed together with springs or by a weight acting through levers.

Figure 8.18 shows a claw or dog clutch. They are used on the drive shafts of lathes and on agricultural machinery.

137

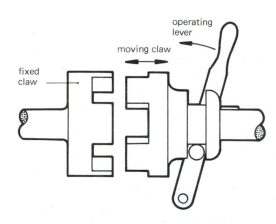

Fig. 8.18   a) A claw or dog clutch   b) A Fischertechnik dog clutch

A saw-tooth clutch is shown engaged in Fig. 8.19. This gives positive drive in one direction only.

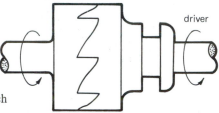

Fig. 8.19   A saw-tooth type clutch

■ Friction Clutches

Friction clutches are used when it is necessary to take up the drive smoothly and to disengage the drive while the shafts are in motion. These two functions can be performed by various clutch systems, e.g. hydraulic or electric clutches. However, the friction system is considered to be one of the most effective.

Fig. 8.20   The friction clutch

a) Clutch disengaged
b) Clutch engaged

c) Fischertechnik friction clutch

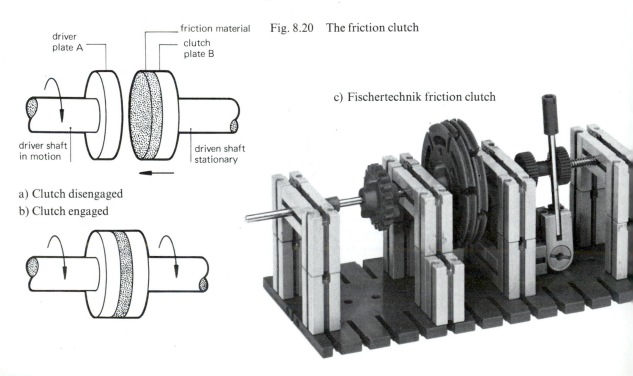

■ The Principle of the Friction Clutch

When plates A and B are held apart, no drive is transmitted. When plate B is moved to contact plate A, drive is transmitted. A non-slip drive of B by A depends on the force that pushes the discs together. If the force is increased, slip is gradually reduced. When the clutch is fully engaged, both discs rotate at the same speed.

There are several different types of friction clutch, but they all operate on the same principle. The cone clutch is shown in Fig. 8.21.

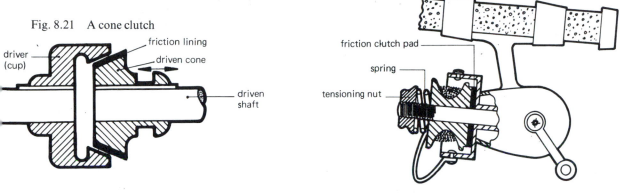

Fig. 8.21   A cone clutch

Fig. 8.22   A simple clutch as used on a fixed-spool fishing reel

The clutch on a fixed-spool fishing reel shows a different clutch arrangement (Fig. 8.22). The clutch allows the reel to slip on the winding shaft. The amount of slip can be altered by adjusting the tensioning nut.

■ The Single-plate Clutch

The **single-plate clutch** is a common type of clutch. It has the advantage of producing a quick disengagement. Pressure is applied by a number of coil springs around the pressure plate. Motion is transmitted from the driver shaft to the driven shaft by the clutch friction plate when this is clamped by the pressure plate. The pressure plate rotates with the driver shaft.

Fig. 8.23   A simple single-plate clutch

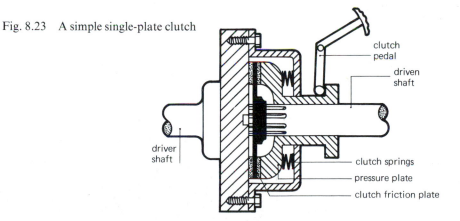

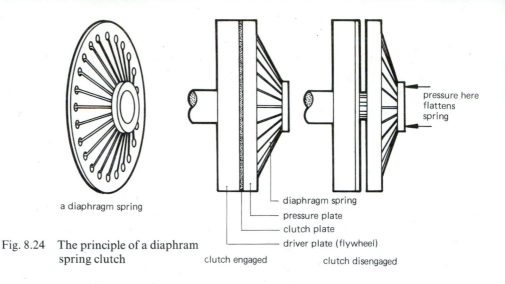

a diaphragm spring

diaphragm spring
pressure plate
clutch plate
driver plate (flywheel)

pressure here
flattens
spring

Fig. 8.24   The principle of a diaphram
             spring clutch

clutch engaged   clutch disengaged

☐ The Diaphragm Spring Clutch

The **diaphragm spring clutch** is a very compact design for a single-plate clutch. It eliminates the need for a series of coil springs by using a diaphragm spring to provide the clamping pressure. The diaphragm is a saucer-shaped disc. It flattens and relieves the pressure when its centre is pressed.

The advantages of a diaphragm clutch are:
1 easier disengagement;
2 suitable for extra-high speeds;
3 fewer parts required;
4 compactness.

☐ Multiple Clutches

Some clutches have to fit into a limited space, for example on motorcycle and in car automatic transmissions. A small single plate would not give enough friction and so a number of friction plates are used. This is called a **multi-plate clutch**. These can operate with weaker springs. This makes them smoother and easier to control.

Fig. 8.25   A multi-plate clutch

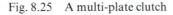

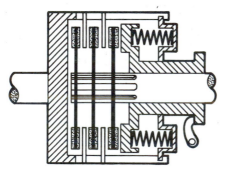

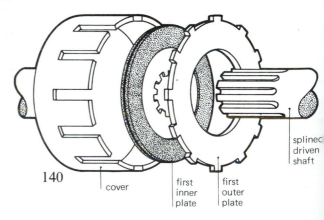

splined
driven
shaft

140

cover

first
inner
plate

first
outer
plate

Multi-plate clutches have increased torque-transmitting ability and, for this reason, are often used in heavy commercial vehicles, racing cars and special purpose military and agricultural vehicles. Multi-plate clutches can be either wet or dry. A wet clutch has oil in the clutch housing to reduce the possibility of fierce engagement.

☐ Clutch Operating Systems

The linkage between the operating pedal or lever and the clutch mechanism may be either mechanical or hydraulic. The **rigid rod and lever** system is not commonly used on vehicles because of the flexible mounting used between transmissions and the vehicle body or frame.

Bowden cables are a popular method of mechanical linkage because they are unaffected by small amounts of movement or vibration. **Hydraulic systems** have a similar advantage. In addition they give smooth quiet operation with little need for attention.

☐ Centrifugal (Automatic) Clutches

Centrifugal clutches do not require any external manual linkage but are operated by 'centrifugal' force. They are designed to engage when the driving shaft reaches a particular speed. Clutches operated in this way are called automatic clutches and are excellent for use on mopeds and motor mowers (Fig. 8.26).

Fig. 8.26   A simple centrifugal clutch   Fig. 8.27   A model centrifugal clutch used on a small vehicle

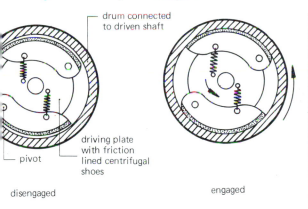

141

9 Lubrication

■ Introduction

Friction prevents two surfaces moving over each other. The friction force can be overcome so that the two surfaces do move over one another. However, the friction force has only been overcome. It has not been removed. Its effects are real and considerable even with 'smooth' contacting surfaces (Fig. 9.1).

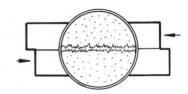

Fig. 9.1   Two pieces of 'smooth' metal seen under a microscope

Friction produces heat and wear. If pressure is applied to the surfaces, the parts become hotter and the rate of wear increases. If the parts become too hot they will weld together.

Lubrication is the introduction of a layer of lubricant to separate the two contacting surfaces. This greatly reduces friction and so reduces heating and wear (Fig. 9.2).

A **lubricant** can be a liquid such as oil or a semi-solid such as grease. Frequently, the layer of lubricant that

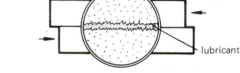

Fig. 9.2   The two pieces of metal are kept apart by the lubricant

separates the surfaces is a thin film estimated at less than 0.008 mm thick.

Oils have to operate under different working conditions of load, speed and temperature. Different oils have different properties. It is therefore necessary to select the correct type of oil for the job (Fig. 9.3).

Fig. 9.3   Oils have to operate under different conditions of load, speed and temperature

In modern engines the oil helps to cool such parts as pistons and bearings. In its passage around the engine, the oil picks up heat from hot parts and must itself be cooled. This is done by the circulation of air around the engine and oil sump or by means of an external cooler.

■ Viscosity

An important property of an oil is its **viscosity** or resistance to flow. Thin oils have a low viscosity and flow easily through small holes and clearances. Thick oils have a high viscosity and offer more resistance to flow or change of their shape. Thus they resist being squeezed out of bearing surfaces at high pressure.

Oil is affected by temperature. It becomes thinner, that is, has a lower viscosity, as it gets hotter. It is important to choose an oil that has a suitable viscosity at the normal operating temperature of, say, an internal combustion engine.

■ Measuring Viscosity

SAE NUMBERS

In America, the Society of Automotive Engineers (SAE) has established a means of classifying oils by their viscosity using numbers. Each SAE number defines the viscosity of the oil at a temperature of 99°C. SAE numbers in no way refer to the quality or any special properties of an oil.

SAE Number	Oil Thickness	Application
10	Extra-light	Lubricating where there is little pressure,
20	Light	e.g. typewriters, sewing machines, duplicating machines.
30	Medium	General purpose lubrication, e.g. engines,
40	Medium-heavy	bearings.
50	Heavy	
60	Extra heavy	Lubricating where there is a lot of
75, 140, 250	Very heavy	pressure, e.g. transmissions and gears

W NUMBERS

A further range of SAE grades has been established to cover the effect of low temperatures upon viscosity. Some oils thicken more than others at low temperatures although they may be within the same grading limits at higher temperatures. Excessively thick oils cause oil drag and give poor lubrication.

The letter **W** indicates that an oil is within a specified viscosity range at a temperature of −18°C. These oils must also be within acceptable limits at 99°C to give protection against excessive thinning at high temperatures. The usual W numbers are SAE 5W, SAE 10W and SAE 20W.

Not long ago it was the practice to use an engine oil with a low viscosity (thin) for winter use and one with a high viscosity (thick) in summer. This meant changing the oil with the seasonal changes of temperature. This is no longer necessary now that multigrade oil is available.

When cold, a multigrade oil has a low viscosity and flows easily at low temperatures. As the engine warms up a change occurs in the oil. This increases the viscosity so that the oil thickens instead of becoming thinner. The oil reverts to its original state as the engine cools down.

This type of oil is given an SAE rating to show its hot and cold viscosities. Two common multigrade oils are SAE 10W/40 and SAE 20W/50.

■ Additives

Lubricants such as engine oils have to withstand many variations of speed, pressure and temperature. The effect of these variations tends to reduce the efficiency of the oil. The addition of certain chemicals improve the lubricant and are called additives. Some of the most important additives are listed below.

a) Oxidation inhibitors.

These reduce the risk of oils oxidising at high temperature.

b) Detergents.

In use, engine oil becomes contaminated and particles can block up oil passages. Detergents make the particles repel each other. They are kept in suspension and are removed with the dirty oil when the oil is changed.

Fig. 9.4   Particles of dirt can block oilways   Fig. 9.5   Detergents prevent particles sticking together

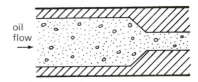

c) Anti-foam agents.

Some engines do not work very well if the oil produces foam. Again it is possible to reduce foaming with suitable additives.

■ Transmission Lubrication

Modern gear assemblies have as little weight and volume as possible. Small gears are subject to high speed and pressure and have only small clearances. Special high viscosity oils are used that enable the gears to operate at these extreme pressures. **Extreme pressure** oils are identified by a suffix EP, e.g. SAE 80 EP and SAE 140 EP.

Greases

These are compounds formed by adding thickeners to lubricating oil. Additives may also provide extra properties such as resistance to breakdown, high temperatures, heavy load or water.

A grease is used where it is impossible to have an oil circulation system, e.g. wheel bearings where disc brakes are fitted.

Methods of Lubricating Mechanisms

There are three basic methods of lubricating mechanisms: gravity feed, splash and force feed.

1 GRAVITY FEED

Figure 9.6 shows gravity feed in its simplest form. One weakness of this method is the fact that the oil hole often becomes blocked with dirt. This may be overcome by using a dustcap, oil cup or one of the other lubricators illustrated in Fig. 9.7.

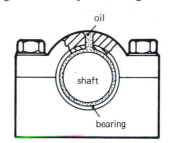

Fig. 9.6   Gravity feed through an oil hole

Fig. 9.7   Lubricators

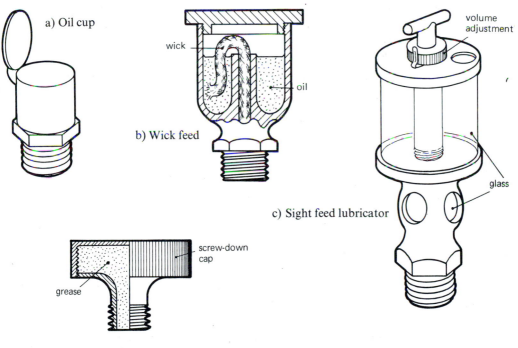

a) Oil cup

b) Wick feed

c) Sight feed lubricator

d) Screw-down greaser

145

cylinder wall

Fig. 9.8   Section through an engine –
the oil in the sump is thrown on to
the cylinder wall by the crankshaft

Fig. 9.9   Section through a gearbox –
oil is picked up from the lowest
gear and passed to the others

2 SPLASH

In this method, the moving parts splash the oil on to the surfaces requiring
lubrication (Figs. 9.8 and 9.9).

3 FORCE FEED

Here the oil is pumped to the moving parts via oil ways or pipes (Fig. 9.10). Oil is
forced along the oil ways by an oil pump (Fig. 9.11). The pressure of the oil can
be found using an oil pressure gauge (Fig. 9.12). Excessive pressure is avoided
by using a pressure relief valve (Fig. 9.13). Often a filter is included in the
system to collect impurities (Fig. 9.14).

Fig. 9.10   Section through an engine showing oil distribution   Fig. 9.11   A gear-type oil pump

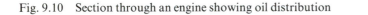

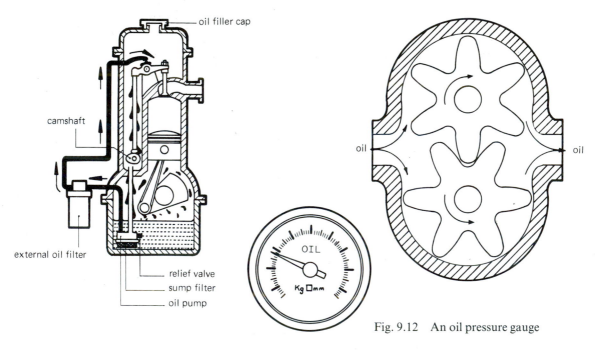

oil filler cap

camshaft

external oil filter

relief valve
sump filter
oil pump

oil

oil

OIL

Kg □mm

Fig. 9.12   An oil pressure gauge

146

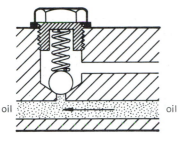

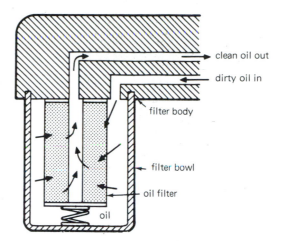

Fig. 9.13   A ball-type oil pressure relief valve

Fig. 9.14   An oil filter collects particles of dirt

A METHOD OF FORCING GREASE INTO BEARING SURFACES

A grease nipple (Fig. 9.15) is screwed into the part to be lubricated. Periodically, grease is forced through the nipple and into the bearing surfaces using a high-pressure grease gun (Fig. 9.16).

Fig. 9.15   An enlarged view of a grease nipple

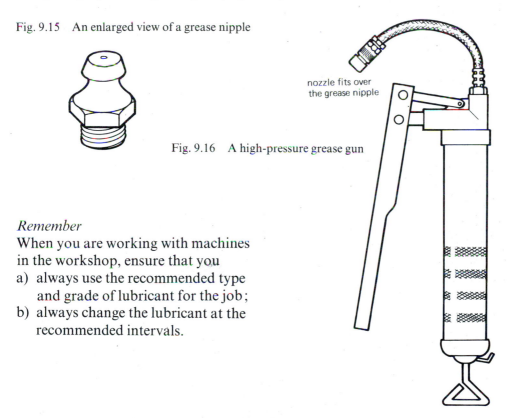

Fig. 9.16   A high-pressure grease gun

Remember

When you are working with machines in the workshop, ensure that you
a) always use the recommended type and grade of lubricant for the job;
b) always change the lubricant at the recommended intervals.

10 Bearings

■ Types of Bearings

A **bearing** is a part of the structure which supports and guides a moving part of a mechanism. There are three basic types of bearing – flat, journal and thrust.

1 FLAT BEARINGS
Flat bearings consist of two or more sliding flat surfaces. These are often used for the bearing surfaces of machine tools. For example, flat bearings are used on the bed and carriage of a lathe, the machine table of a milling machine, and the ram and slides of a shaping machine (Fig. 10.1).

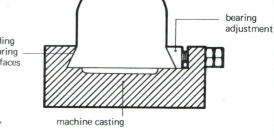

Fig. 10.1   The bearing surfaces of a shaping machine – flat bearing

2 JOURNAL BEARINGS
When a bearing supports a cylindrical shaft it is called a **journal bearing** (Fig. 10.2). This type of bearing can carry radial loads only.

Fig. 10.2   A journal bearing

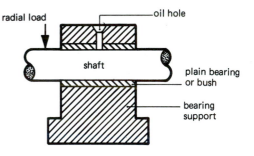

3 THRUST BEARINGS
When a bearing takes the longitudinal or axial load on a shaft, it is called a **thrust bearing** (Fig. 10.3).

Fig. 10.3   A thrust bearing

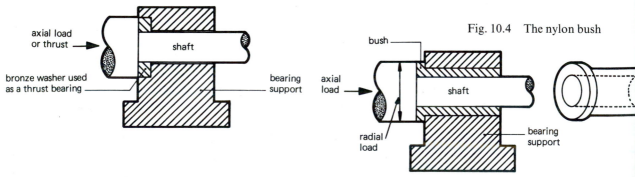

Fig. 10.4   The nylon bush

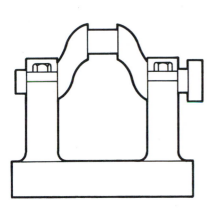

Fig. 10.5   Split bearings used to support
a crankshaft

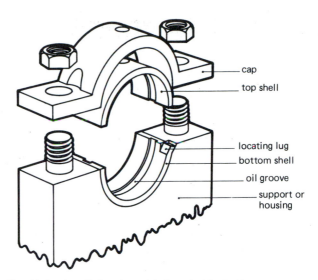

cap
top shell
locating lug
bottom shell
oil groove
support or
housing

Fig. 10.6   A split bearing with detachable shells

Some bearings are designed to take longitudinal and radial loads. For example, the nylon bush (Fig. 10.4) will take longitudinal and radial loads.

To provide a suitable combination of materials, to minimise friction and wear, and to provide a simple and inexpensive way of repairing a worn or damaged bearing, a sleeve called a **bush** is fitted in the hole of the bearing support. Bushes are usually made a very tight fit in the hole, so that all movement and wear take place between the bush and the shaft. Figures 10.2 and 10.4 show this type of bush in use.

A bush can only be used when the part of the shaft which runs in it can be inserted from one end. If the shaft is of such a shape, for example an engine crankshaft (Fig. 10.5), that this is not possible, the bearing must be split. A split bearing is shown in Fig. 10.6. The two halves of the bearing are held together by bolts, studs or screws. In this case, the equivalent of the bush is known as a pair of bearing shells.

Journal and thrust bearings are usually one of two types:
a) plain bearings or bushes;
b) ball or roller bearings.

■ **Plain Bearings**

Plain bearings are one of the simplest types of bearing. They consist of a plain hole in the supporting component in which the shaft rotates. This method is effective when only moderate speeds and loads are involved. This is frequently the case when items are of plastic construction. Nylon is often used for plain bearings. Other suitable materials are cast iron, brass and aluminium if the holes are suitably lubricated.

☐ Plain Bearing Materials

Shafts are usually made of steel which may be soft or hard according to the conditions to be encountered in service. For a given shaft a decision has to be made on the most suitable mating material for the bearing. The most commonly used materials are discussed below.

BRONZE

Bronzes are primarily alloys of copper and tin. A type commonly used contains a small amount of phosphorous and is known as phosphor-bronze. Bronzes are fairly hard, though softer than steel, and have good load carrying capacity but are less suited than some other materials to high rubbing speeds.

WHITE METAL

This is basically an alloy of tin with small amounts of copper and antimony. Since white metal is soft, it adapts itself closely to the shape of the shaft. If the bearing does become overheated the metal melts and runs, leaving the shaft undamaged and giving warning of what has happened. The softness of the metal has a disadvantage in that it has limited load carrying capacity. White metal is sometimes bonded directly on to the bearing housing. However, it is now more common to use detachable shells (Fig. 10.6). These shells have a 'backing' of steel with a thin lining of white metal.

CAST IRON

Cast iron is used to form a flat or sliding bearing. Fortunately, two cast iron surfaces will run together and make an excellent bearing. If this were not so, the construction of machine tools would be much more difficult and expensive. No other metal will run with itself as a bearing. It is probably the graphite in the structure of the cast iron that allows it to do so.

SINTERED BEARINGS

These are bushes made from oil-soaked powder of copper, tin and graphite that have been pressed into shape when hot.

PLASTIC, NYLON, COMPOSITE AND PTFE-COATED BEARINGS

Bearings from these materials tend to be quiet, are cheap to produce and do not corrode.

AIR

Air pressure is sometimes used to support a moving part. Although this method is not very common, it performs the same task as the more usual bearings. A hovercraft moves on an air bearing as do certain types of vacuum cleaner and lawn mower. Air can be used in flat (sliding) bearing applications.

■ The Lubrication of Plain Journal Bearings

When a bearing is properly lubricated, a thin film of oil separates the bearing from the shaft. When the shaft is at rest, it lies in contact with the bearing in the direction of the load (Fig. 10.7).

When the shaft rotates, the wedge effect of the oil forces it between the shaft and the bearing, stopping metal to metal contact (Fig. 10.8).

In the area opposite that of greater pressure, there is very little pressure. It is in this region that oil must be fed to the bearing (Figs. 10.7 and 10.8).

Fig. 10.7   A shaft at rest   Fig. 10.8   A shaft in motion

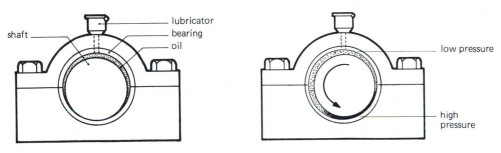

Note In both diagrams the clearance between the shaft and bearing has been exaggerated for clarity.

■ Ball and Roller Bearings

The action in ball and roller bearings is not that of rubbing, but rolling between the balls or rollers and their races. The inner race is fixed to the shaft and the outer race is mounted in a bearing support housing. There is usually a **cage** to prevent adjacent balls or rollers from rubbing against one another.

The races and balls or rollers are made from a special quality steel, suitably hardened. Cages may be made of bronze, aluminium or mild steel.

BALL BEARINGS
Figure 10.10 shows a single row bearing with the balls running in grooves in the races. This is called a **ballrace**. It is intended for carrying mainly radial loads. Double row bearings of this type are capable of carrying heavier loads.

Fig. 10.9   End view of a shaft supported by a ball or roller bearing

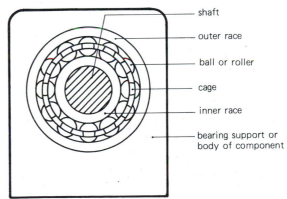

151

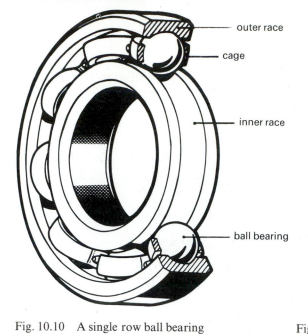
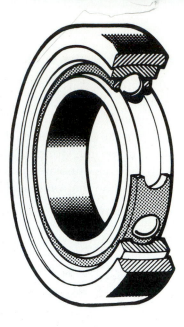

outer race

cage

inner race

ball bearing

Fig. 10.10   A single row ball bearing
Fig. 10.12   An angular contact ball bearing

Fig. 10.11   A self-aligning ball bearing
Fig. 10.13   A thrust bearing

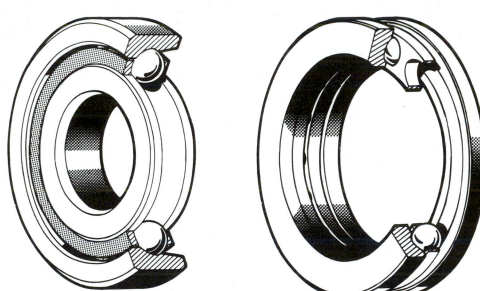

SELF-ALIGNING BEARINGS

Self-aligning bearings allow the shaft to run at a slight angle to the housing axis and are used where precise alignment cannot be maintained (Fig. 10.11).

ANGULAR CONTACT BEARINGS

Angular contact bearings are capable of taking radial loads, and axial loads in one direction only (Fig. 10.12). They are generally used in pairs and must be fitted the correct way round.

THRUST BEARINGS

Thrust bearings are capable of taking axial thrust loads (Fig. 10.13). The axial thrust is taken by hardened steel balls, supported in a cage, and moving in circular grooves ground in hardened steel plates.

CYLINDRICAL ROLLER JOURNAL BEARINGS

Roller journal bearings are capable of carrying greater radial loads than ball bearings but no axial load (Fig. 10.14). Where heavy radial loads have to be carried at low speed, especially long rollers of small diameter (called **needle rollers**) may be used (Fig. 10.15).

Fig. 10.14   A roller journal bearing   Fig. 10.15   A needle roller bearing

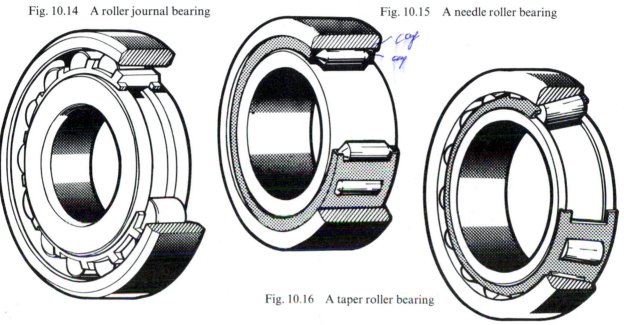

Fig. 10.16   A taper roller bearing

TAPER ROLLER BEARINGS

Figure 10.16 shows a taper roller bearing. The working surfaces of both races and rollers are conical.

Taper roller bearings are always used in pairs facing each other and are capable of dealing with considerable axial and radial loads. They are provided with some axial adjustment to control the amount of play.

■ Important Points Concerning all Bearings

1   Cleanliness of all parts is important when fitting.
2   Bearings should be fitted and removed using the proper tools.
3   Bearings should be protected from dust, etc., if used in an exposed position.
4   Bearings should be adjusted when necessary or replaced if worn bearings have no means of adjustment.
5   Bearings should be lubricated according to a recommended procedure.

11 Steering

■ Introduction

Almost all wheeled vehicles need to have a steering system to enable them to change direction when in motion. Some vehicles have a very simple system. Others require extremely complex geometry and linkages.

Fig. 11.1   The need for steering mechanisms

Note that in many of the diagrams in this section, dimensions and angles have been exaggerated to enable the principles to be more easily understood.

■ Steering Requirements

Efficient steering plays an important part in the safe handling of a vehicle. The steering must be responsive, light to handle and the wheels should have a tendency to return to the straight ahead position after a turn. Most vehicles have front-wheel steering because rear-wheel steering causes four main problems.

1   The wheels have to point in the opposite direction to that in which the vehicle is travelling.
2   If a vehicle is parked near the kerb, the rear wheels have to mount the kerb when it is driven away (Fig. 11.2).

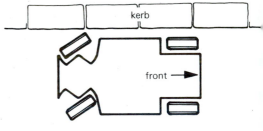

Fig. 11.2   A car with rear-wheel steering

3   The width of the body and thus seating area have to be reduced to allow for movement of the wheels.
4   The vehicle can turn very quickly. This is dangerous because it makes the vehicle difficult to control at high speeds.

Design requirements for industrial vehicles are different from those for passenger cars. Therefore rear-wheel steering is frequently found on dumper and fork-lift trucks because the front wheels take most of the weight and cannot be used for steering.

The remainder of this section is confined to front-wheel steering systems.

■ Track and Wheelbase

On a four-wheeled vehicle, the distance between the wheels on the same axle is called the **track**. The distance between the front and rear wheels is called the **wheelbase** (Fig. 11.3).

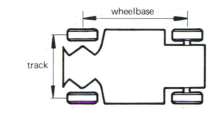

Fig. 11.3   Basic steering terms for a small vehicle

■ The Swinging Beam System

This is one of the earliest and simplest steering systems. It is found on horsedrawn vehicles, road rollers (Fig. 11.4) and luggage trolleys. It enables the vehicle to have a very small turning circle. It is not suitable for use on fast vehicles because it causes wheel scrubbing and instability if used at high speed. A lot of clearance is required under the vehicle to allow the axle to pivot.

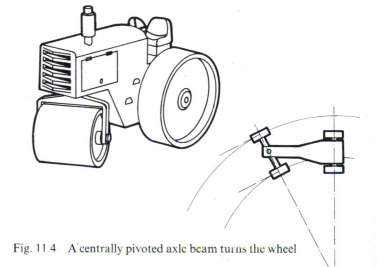

Fig. 11.4   A centrally pivoted axle beam turns the wheel

■ The Ackermann System

In 1818 Rudolph Ackermann took out a patent on a steering system which is now widely used. Basically it consists of two short hinged stub axles connected by a track rod (Fig. 11.5). When a vehicle turns, the inner front wheel must move through a greater angle than the outer wheel to avoid tyre wear and skidding. This is achieved by inclining the steering arms at an angle. The angle is found by drawing a line from the king pin to the centre of the rear axle. Both wheels are parallel when the vehicle is travelling in a straight line. As the wheels are turned, a difference in wheel angle occurs (Fig. 11.6).

Fig. 11.5   The Ackermann principle

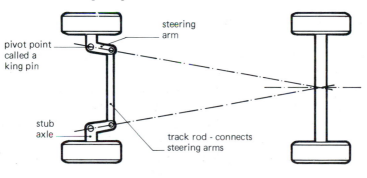

155

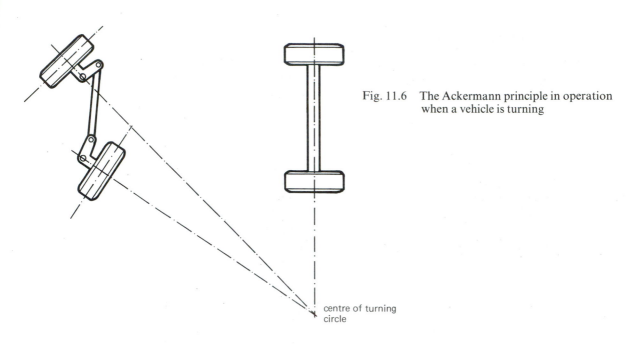

Fig. 11.6   The Ackermann principle in operation when a vehicle is turning

centre of turning circle

Figures 11.7 and 11.8 show different arrangements based on the Ackermann principle. Some vehicles have a more complex mechanism because the brakes and suspension system are often incorporated in this area.

Fig. 11.7   A traction engine steering joint

Fig. 11.8   A tractor steering joint, steering arm and ball joint and track rod

The Stub Axle Steering Joint

The stub axle has a simple hinged joint pivoting on a steel pin called a **king pin**. The illustration in Fig. 11.9 shows a typical kart steering joint. The road wheel is fitted to the stub axle by means of a hub and taper roller bearings.

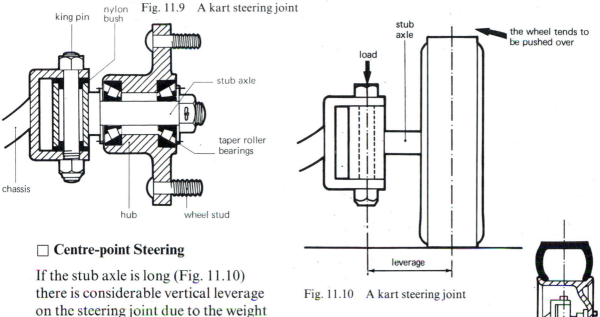

Fig. 11.9   A kart steering joint

Centre-point Steering

If the stub axle is long (Fig. 11.10) there is considerable vertical leverage on the steering joint due to the weight of the vehicle. There is also considerable horizontal leverage causing difficult steering when the brakes are applied. This leverage creates stress and wear on the parts.

Fig. 11.10   A kart steering joint

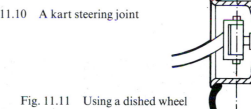

Fig. 11.11   Using a dished wheel

These problems are overcome by reducing the leverage with a dished wheel (Fig. 11.11). However, there is rarely enough room within a dished wheel to fit brakes and bearings. As a compromise solution, the wheel is made less dished than in Fig. 11.11 and the remaining stress is removed from the steering joint by altering the geometry of the parts. The stub axle and king pin are inclined so that the centre line of the wheel and king pin meet at a common point at ground level (Fig. 11.12). This is termed 'centre-point steering'.

Fig. 11.12   Sloping the king pin and wheel

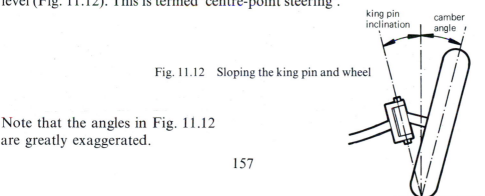

Note that the angles in Fig. 11.12 are greatly exaggerated.

157

☐ Camber

To obtain centre-point steering (Fig. 11.12), the wheel is tilted outwards at the top. The angle between the wheel and the vertical is called the **camber angle**. Figure 11.12 shows a wheel with positive camber. When wheels are vertical this is called 'neutral camber'. When wheels are tilted in at the top this is called negative camber. Wheels on the same axle always have the same camber angle.

Figure 11.12 shows a wheel with too much positive camber. This causes uneven tyre wear when driving in a straight line. When the vehicle is cornering, the tyre rolls under inwards. This causes poor road contact, tyre squeal and overheating.

Many high performance cars are designed with slight negative camber. This combats the effects of tyre roll when cornering hard and also improves the road-holding ability of the vehicle.

☐ Castor

Castor causes a steering system to be self-centring. Wheel castor ensures that a vehicle travels in a straight line unless a torque is applied to the steering wheel. The action is similar to that found on the castors of a supermarket trolley (Fig. 11.13a). When a force is exerted on the trolley, the wheel moves in the direction of the force. The wheel follows the path taken by the pivot centre line. The pivot centre line is always in front of the wheel.

On a vehicle, a castor can be obtained either by mounting a vertical king pin in front of the wheel (Fig. 11.13b) or by inclining the king pin forward at the bottom by an amount known as the **castor angle** (Fig. 11.13c).

Fig. 11.13   Castor action

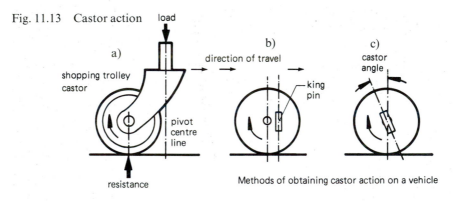

☐ Wheel Alignment

A plan view of a vehicle should show both wheels parallel when in the straight ahead position. But allowance must be made for clearance in the steering joints. This clearance is taken up by the splaying out or in of the wheels. The allowance is called 'toe-in', if the distance between the front of the wheels at centre height is less than the distance between the rear of the wheels at centre height (Fig. 11.14).

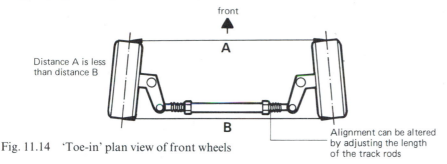

Fig. 11.14 'Toe-in' plan view of front wheels

Rear-wheel drive vehicles normally have 'toe-in'.
Front-wheel drive vehicles normally have 'toe-out'.
This adjustment is made by altering the length of the track rods. The exact amount of adjustment is always very small and is indicated in each manufacturer's vehicle manual.

■ Steering Mechanisms

Figure 11.15 shows a simple steering system fitted to a kart. The steering wheel is connected to the road wheels by a mechanical linkage. Movement of the steering wheel gives a similar movement to the road wheels. This is called **direct steering**.

Fig. 11.15   A kart steering mechanism

159

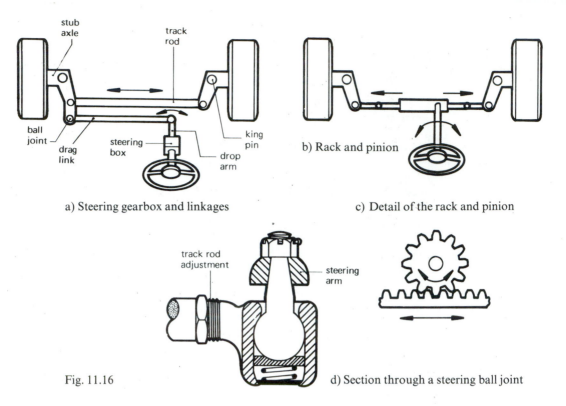

a) Steering gearbox and linkages   c) Detail of the rack and pinion

Fig. 11.16   d) Section through a steering ball joint

A large vehicle is too heavy to steer in this way and so a steering gearbox is used (Fig. 11.16a). This enables the driver to exert a large force on the front wheels with the minimum of effort at the steering wheel. A steering box consists of a worm which is rotated by the steering wheel. A nut engages with the worm. The nut's movement on the worm is transmitted to the wheels to turn them. Gear ratios vary from 10:1 on light cars to 30:1 on heavy lorries. As the ratio is lowered, a larger number of turns of the steering wheel is required to move the wheels from lock to lock. Some heavy vehicles are fitted with power-assisted steering to further reduce the effort required to turn them.

Motion is transmitted from the steering wheel to the steering box by the **steering column**. Movement is transmitted from the steering box to the road wheels by a system of levers called **track rods**. The track rods are connected by **ball joints**. These allow universal movement at the joints (Fig. 11.16d).

■ Rack and Pinion Steering

An alternative to a steering gearbox is a rack and pinion arrangement (Fig. 11.16b). This gives a very positive steering movement.

□ Centripetal Force and its Effect on Vehicle Steering

Most vehicles have pneumatic tyres. When subjected to a side force these tyres distort and affect the steering characteristics of the vehicle (Fig. 11.17b).

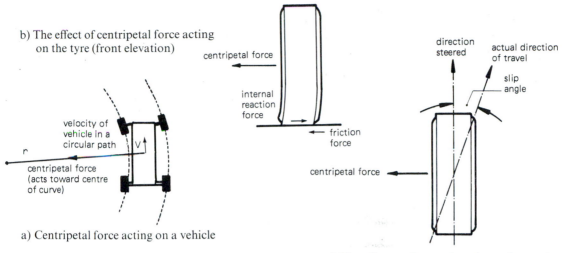

b) The effect of centripetal force acting on the tyre (front elevation)

centripetal force

internal
reaction
force

friction
force

centripetal force

direction
steered

actual direction
of travel

slip
angle

velocity of
vehicle in a
circular path

r

centripetal force
(acts toward centre
of curve)

a) Centripetal force acting on a vehicle

c) The effect on the steering when a force acts on a tyre

Fig. 11.17   Centripetal force and its effect on vehicle steering

Newton's First Law of Motion states that an object will continue to move with uniform linear motion unless acted upon by an external force. Such an external force must be applied to a vehicle to make it move in a circle. This force is called a centripetal force as it acts towards the centre of the circle of movement (Fig. 11.17a). Centripetal force causes change of direction, not change of speed. It is an accelerating force.

When a vehicle is required to turn a corner, its front wheels are turned so that they are at an angle to the straight line in which the vehicle would like to continue to travel (First Law). A friction force between the tyres and the road results. This force does two things. It provides the centripetal force which makes the vehicle change direction. It also distorts the pneumatic tyre of the vehicle in much the same way that a diver standing on the end of a springboard distorts its shape by bending it (Fig. 11.17b).

When a tyre is distorted, a vehicle's direction of travel is affected. The amount of deflection is called the **slip angle** (Fig. 11.17c). A side force caused by wind, friction force or road camber produces a slip angle at each tyre. Tyre slip angles cause oversteer or understeer.

When the rear wheel slip angles are greater than those at the front, the vehicle turns more sharply than normal. This is called **oversteer**. It is corrected by the driver straightening up the steering wheel (Fig. 11.18a).

When the front wheel slip angles are greater than those at the rear, the vehicle takes a wider path than normal. This is called **understeer**. It is corrected by the driver steering further into the bend (Fig. 11.18b).

Fig. 11.18   Oversteer and understeer

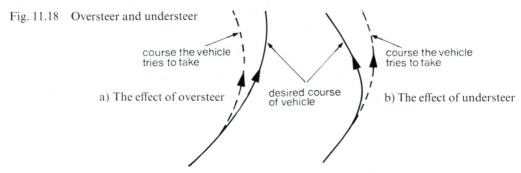

course the vehicle
tries to take

course the vehicle
tries to take

a) The effect of oversteer

desired course
of vehicle

b) The effect of understeer

These effects are hardly noticeable to the driver under normal circumstances. However, if a vehicle skids on icy roads, an oversteering car usually goes into a rear-wheel skid, while an understeering car usually goes into a front-wheel skid.

■ Construction Kits

Most of the steering mechanisms described in this chapter can be made using Fischertechnik or Meccano components.

MECCANO
A simple steering mechanism suitable for small vehicles and models can be made from Meccano perforated strips and angle brackets (Fig. 11.19).

Fig. 11.19   A simple steering mechanism made with Meccano components

Small vehicles that require maximum manoeuvrability, such as delivery vans or fork-lift trucks, use castor steering mechanisms (Fig. 11.20).

Fig. 11.20   Castor steering mechanisms

FISCHERTECHNIK
Simple steering mechanisms can be made with Fischertechnik components.
Figure 11.21a shows a simple luggage trolley steering mechanism. Small vehicle
steering mechanisms are shown in Fig. 11.21b and c.

Fig. 11.21

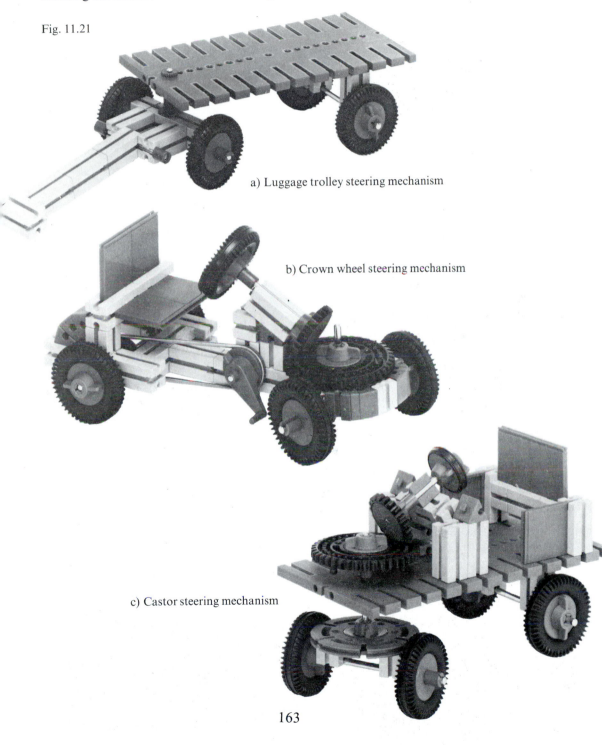

a) Luggage trolley steering mechanism

b) Crown wheel steering mechanism

c) Castor steering mechanism

12 Complex Mechanisms

■ The Need for a Differential Gearbox

When a vehicle turns a corner, the outer rear wheel must travel further than the inner wheel in the same time (Fig. 12.1).

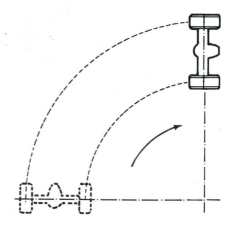

Therefore, the outer wheel must turn faster than the inner wheel. If a solid or 'live' rear axle connects both wheels, this is not possible and the vehicle tends to continue in the straight ahead direction. Alternatively, the inner wheel skids causing rapid tyre wear, noise and instability of the vehicle.

Fig. 12.1   Rear wheels turning a corner

The problem can be solved by driving one wheel and allowing the other to run free. The unbalanced driving thrust of this system would not be acceptable on a motorcar, but the system is useful when constructing models.

The most widely used solution to the problem is to use a **differential gearbox**. This mechanism allows the wheels to rotate at different speeds while maintaining a positive drive to both wheels. The inner wheel slows down while the outer wheel speeds up by the same amount.

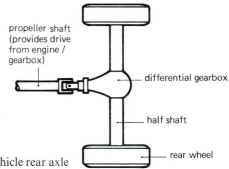

propeller shaft (provides drive from engine / gearbox)

differential gearbox

half shaft

rear wheel

Fig. 12.2   Layout of a vehicle rear axle

■ The Principle of a Differential Gearbox

When the vehicle is moving straight forward, the **crown wheel** of the differential is driven by the **propeller shaft**. The crown wheel rotates the complete bevel gear cage (Fig. 12.3).

When a vehicle turns a corner, the inner wheel slows down. This causes the planet wheels to rotate on their own axes. Both half shafts are driven even though they rotate at different speeds.

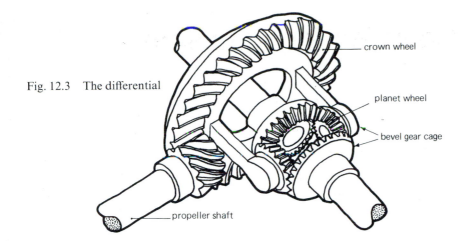

Fig. 12.3   The differential

crown wheel

planet wheel

bevel gear cage

propeller shaft

■ Differentials for Practical Work

A complete working differential is available in the Fischertechnik construction kit (Fig. 12.4) or Fischertechnik components can be used to build a differential gearbox (Fig. 12.5). This enables the differential action to be fully understood.

Fig. 12.4 a)   The Fischertechnik differential with the inner gearing exposed.

Fig. 12.4 b)   Power unit connected to a Fischertechnik differential (nearside wheel is removed)

165

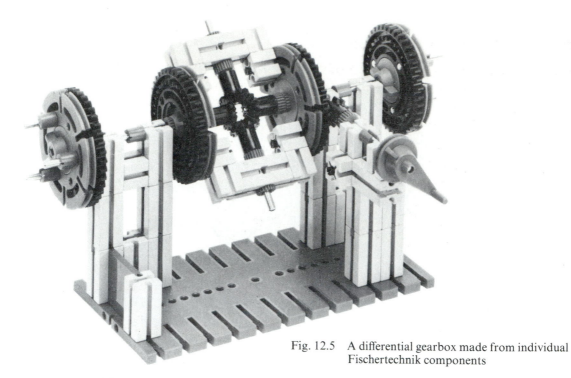

Fig. 12.5   A differential gearbox made from individual Fischertechnik components

The action of a differential gearbox can also be appreciated by building one with Meccano gears (Fig. 12.6). Here a mixture of contrate gears and pinions is used. However, all the gears could be bevel gears.

The drive from the propeller shaft to the Meccano differential gearbox is through a pinion gear and a contrate gear (Fig. 12.7).

Fig. 12.6   Using contrate gears to build a differential gearbox

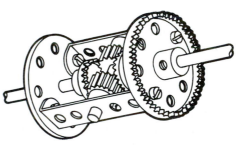

Fig. 12.7   Drive from the propeller shaft to the back wheels using a Meccano differential

■ Motor Vehicle Power Transmission

Many ways of transmitting torque have been described. Several of these mechanisms are used on a motor vehicle to transmit torque from the engine to the driving wheels. Figure 12.8 shows a typical transmission system for a front-engined, rear-wheel drive vehicle.

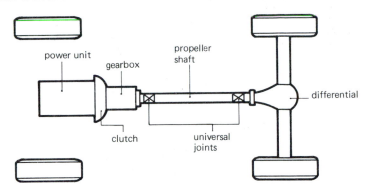

Fig. 12.8   A motor vehicle transmission system

The main features of this transmission system can be identified as follows.

The **engine** produces the power to propel the vehicle. The engine provides torque to rotate the propeller shaft.

The **clutch** enables the torque to be connected to or isolated from the transmission.

The **gearbox** allows alternative gear ratios to be used and also enables the vehicle to be reversed.

The **universal joints** allow for suspension movement of the rear axle.

The **propeller shaft** transmits torque from the gearbox to the differential.

The **differential** allows for a speed difference of the rear wheels when cornering. It also transmits the torque through 90°.

The **half shafts** connect the differential to each wheel.

■ Cams

Linear, rotary, reciprocating or oscillating motion can be transmitted by the use of a cam. Figure 12.9 shows some different types of cam mechanisms.

Fig. 12.9

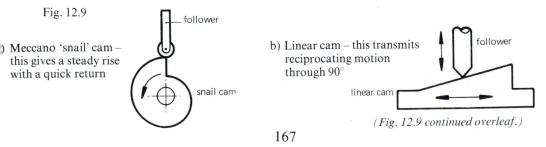

a) Meccano 'snail' cam – this gives a steady rise with a quick return

b) Linear cam – this transmits reciprocating motion through 90°

(Fig. 12.9 continued overleaf.)

167

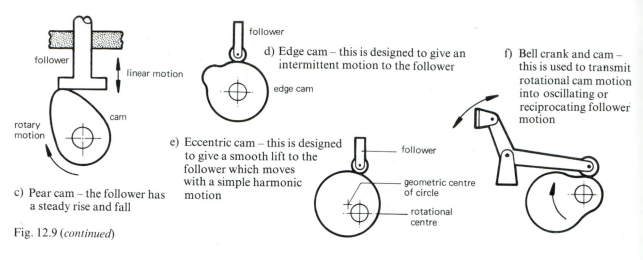

d) Edge cam – this is designed to give an intermittent motion to the follower

f) Bell crank and cam – this is used to transmit rotational cam motion into oscillating or reciprocating follower motion

e) Eccentric cam – this is designed to give a smooth lift to the follower which moves with a simple harmonic motion

c) Pear cam – the follower has a steady rise and fall

Fig. 12.9 (*continued*)

■ Linkages

The path traced out by a moving point is called the **locus** of the point. For example, if a mass is hung by a string from a fixed point and allowed to oscillate freely (pendulum arrangement), the locus of the mass is an arc of a circle (Fig. 12.10).

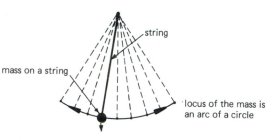

Fig. 12.10   The locus of a mass swinging on a string

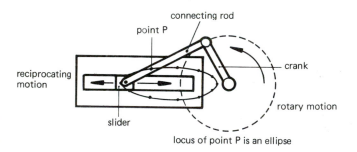

Fig. 12.11   The crank and slider linkage

Fig. 12.12   The four-bar chain linkage

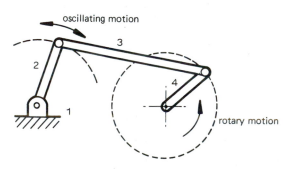
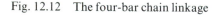

Several linkages have been described earlier in this book. The crank and slider linkage is used to convert rotary motion of the crank into reciprocating motion of the slider and vice versa (Fig. 12.11). The locus of point *P* on the connecting rod is an ellipse.

The four-bar chain linkage is used to convert rotary motion into oscillating motion and vice versa (Fig. 12.12). The linkage consists of three moving levers and a fourth fixed lever or frame. The ground is the fourth fixed reference frame, hence the name a four-bar chain.

An example of a four-bar chain is the treadle drive used on sewing machines, grindstones and lathes before the introduction of electric

168

motors (Fig. 12.13). The worker's foot
provided an input oscillating motion.
This was transformed into rotary
motion output.

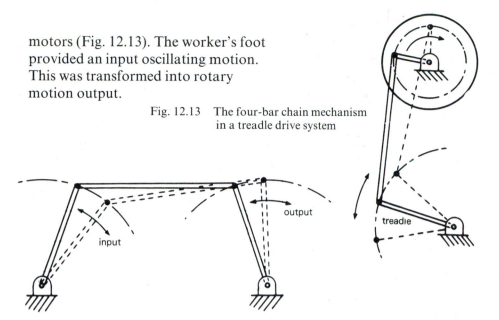

Fig. 12.13   The four-bar chain mechanism
in a treadle drive system

Fig. 12.14   The four-bar chain – oscillating input, oscillating output

Movement in an arc is produced when a four-bar chain is used to transmit
oscillating motion (Fig. 12.14). This type of motion is found in a children's
playground rocking horse (Fig. 12.15).

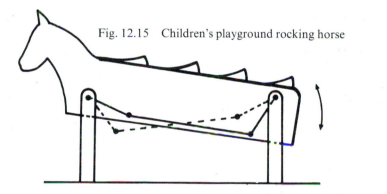

Fig. 12.15   Children's playground rocking horse

The 'X' type linkage is useful when a
level platform of adjustable height is
required, e.g. an ironing board (Fig.
12.16) or a projector stand.

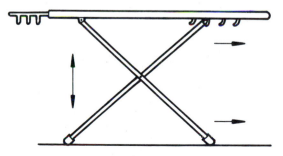

Fig. 12.16   The 'X' type linkage used for an ironing board

The mechanism used for an 'up and over' garage door consists of rollers and vertical and horizontal tracks. The top edge of the door is attached to a roller which moves along a horizontal track in the garage roof (Fig. 12.17). Another roller attached lower down the door moves up and down a vertical track. The locus of the lower edge of the garage door is a parabola.

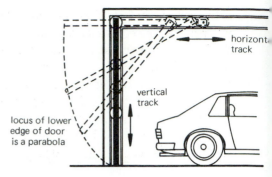

Fig. 12.17   An 'up and over' garage door mechanism

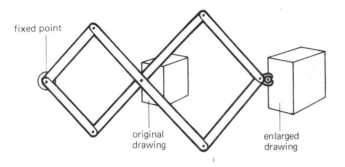

Fig. 12.18   A pantograph

A pantograph is a linkage made up of one or more parallelograms (Fig. 12.18). It is used when copying drawings to a larger scale.

The crank and slotted lever mechanism was described in Section 6. The mechanism is often used as a quick return mechanism for shaping machines and surface grinding machines (Fig. 12.19).

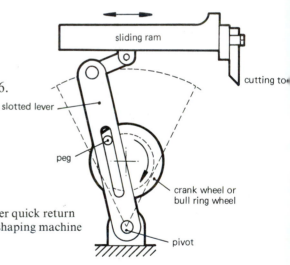

Fig. 12.19   The crank and slotted lever quick return mechanism as used on a shaping machine

Fig. 12.20   The Davis steering gear

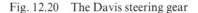

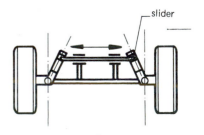

Several steering mechanisms were described in Section 11. A further example is the **Davis steering gear** (Fig. 12.20). This allows the inner wheel to turn through a greater angle than the outer wheel when cornering.

Pawl and ratchet mechanisms are often used to control rotary motion, e.g. ensuring that a shaft can only rotate in one direction (Fig. 12.21a). This type of ratchet mechanism is used in the winding mechanism of a mechanical wrist watch, a fishing reel or in a ratchet brace. Ratchet mechanisms can be used to produce an **intermittent drive** of a rotating shaft (Fig. 12.21b). The shaft is rotated by a pawl on a drive arm engaging with a ratchet wheel. The rotary motion is in steps equal to the number of ratchet teeth the pawl passes over on its return stroke. An intermittent drive is used on the machine table feed mechanism of a shaping machine.

Fig. 12.21   Ratchet mechanism

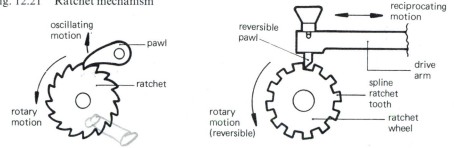

Intermittent motion is a feature of the ratchet mechanism used in clock escapement mechanisms (Fig. 12.22). A ratchet wheel or escapement wheel is driven in a clockwise direction by a spring or a weight. The **escapement wheel** engages with pawls or pallets attached to a pendulum. The periodic motion of the pawls is controlled by the oscillating pendulum. Small clocks and watches have a balance wheel to control the periodic motion of the pallets.

Fig. 12.22   A simple clock escapement

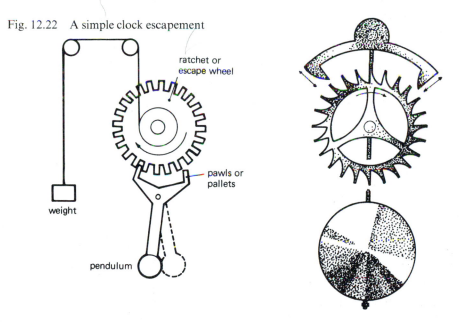

171

☐ Gearboxes and Reversing Mechanisms

Motor drives to small vehicles and winding mechanisms often require a reversing mechanism. A method of reversing a drive is shown in Fig. 12.23. The motor drive is taken to a shaft with two pinion gears. The drive is transmitted through a right angle by a contrate gear meshed with one of the pinion gears. The drive can be put in forward or reverse by moving a pivoted lever which engages either of the pinions with the contrate gear. This is a 1 : 1 ratio reversing mechanism, that is, the forward and reverse drive speeds are the same.

Fig. 12.23   A reversing mechanism (ratio 1:1)

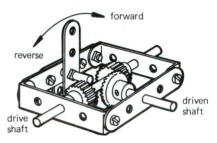

Fig. 12.24   An alternative reversing mechanism

An alternative form of reversing mechanism is shown in Fig. 12.24. Forward or reverse output movement is obtained by moving a pivoted lever.

If gear wheels and pinions with different numbers of teeth are used, it is possible to build a two-speed gearbox (Fig. 12.25). A lever sliding action is used to select the two different gear ratios.

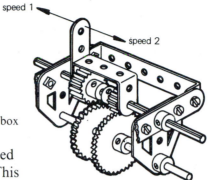

Fig. 12.25   A two-speed gearbox

It is also possible to combine a two-speed gearbox with a reversing mechanism. This gearbox will then provide two forward speeds and one reverse speed (Fig. 12.26). Note the use of an idler gear to provide the reversing mechanism.

Fig. 12.26   A gearbox with two forward speeds and one reverse speed

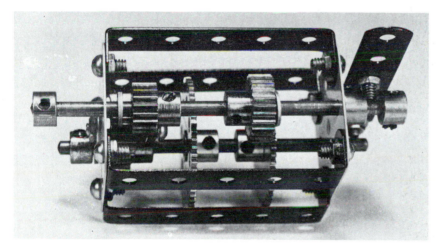

Acknowledgments

For permission to reproduce certain photographs and diagrams in this book, the authors and publishers would like to thank the following:

Fischertechnik (Figs. 2.34, 4.33, 5.40a and 12.4a); BP Educational Service (Figs. 3.3, 4.8, 4.12, 4.13, 4.15, 4.17, 4.18 and 4.19 from BP Wallchart No. W25); Barlow & Chidlaw Ltd (Figs. 4.44 and 4.45); The Davall Gear Company Ltd (Figs. 4.46 and 4.47); Rover Triumph (Figs. 5.22 and 5.23).

E. Ryan
O/No. 864/51
£11.50 (net-)